MY HAND IS

Elastic

My Hand is *Elastic*

Award-winning entries
from the 1993
W H Smith
Young Writers' Competition

PAN MACMILLAN
CHILDREN'S BOOKS

First published 1994 by Pan Macmillan Children's Books

a division of Pan Macmillan Publishers Limited
Cavaye Place London SW10 9PG
and Basingstoke

Associated companies throughout the world

ISBN 0 333 60636 1

1 3 5 7 9 8 6 4 2

A CIP catalogue record for this book is available from
the British Library.

Phototypeset by Intype, London
Printed by Cox & Wyman Ltd, Reading

'Book' from *Sing for the Taxman* (Seren Books, 1993) by Sheenagh Pugh
reproduced by kind permission of Seren Books.

CONTENTS

INTRODUCTION

It is always a pleasure to celebrate success. To celebrate the achievements of no fewer than seventy-three people is a real joy.

The seventy-three writers in this book were chosen by our judges from the 30,000 entries to the 1993 W H Smith Young Writers' Competition. In fact, seventy-three is a record, since it is the highest number of winners in one year since the competition began in 1959.

The list of past winners who are now professional writers grows each year. Jan Mark, who won a Young Writers award in 1959, is now a competition judge. The poet Sheenagh Pugh also won a major award in the competition at eight years old, and again in 1965 when she was thirteen. It was a pleasure to discover a recent poem of hers, 'Book', in which she says so many of the things I feel about reading:

> I am the thought that flies in seconds
> through a man's head, and lives for ever.
>
> I am all he knew: I am his words
> on the other side of the world,
> sounding long after he dies.
>
> I can cure the sick; build bridges,
> change your mind, choke you with tears.
> I can make a world, and man it.

Give me to a child, I am the ocean
cupped in his hands: I am all the sand
of the beach in his toy bucket.
I am the key to the walled garden,
the magic lamp, the island
where the treasure is.

I am could-be and might-have-been,
the story of the people, the store
of seed-corn. I feed the hunger
that grain leaves keen.

The thrill of reading a good, thick novel or some fine poetry
is a journey, an adventure. You live the lives of other people.
You experience sadness, fear, excitement. To be able to write
fiction and poetry which make the reader 'live' someone else's
experiences is a tremendous gift.

We live in an age of television, video and that menace to
proper, developed thought, the 'sound bite'. Yet, although
the spoken word can make an impact, the written word is
more considered and long-lasting. It is a more reliable record
of a person's true mind. A major award-winner in this year's
competition, Richard Attfield, is autistic, from him we learn:

'Within I am the same as ordinary people. Other
people do not see the you within. People do not
realize my ability. I am the one who within realizes
intelligent I am . . . If I write about my problems
people will understand and then given time autism will
win no more.' He goes on to say: 'Words are my
friends. I am never autistic when I write.'

Richard cannot tell us this face to face. But, armed with
a special computer, the Canon Communicator, he can set
down words which make us pay attention. We can return to

his piece and give it more thought. This is the power of the written word.

Richard's gifts as a writer are considerable, but his success has been ensured by his parents who have supported and encouraged him. Indeed, all the young writers in this book owe much to parents and teachers. Without them there would have been no good books or lively discussion, no advice or praise for their writing, all so important in developing a love of language and ideas.

The greatest contributors to the success of the competition, of course, are the young writers themselves. So much excellent and varied work floods in that the judges' task is extremely difficult. They must select between sixty and seventy pieces from the tens of thousands which come in – just enough to fill a book. They could so easily publish a ten-volume encyclopaedia each year!

This year, in addition to seventy-three prizewinners, over 1800 young people received commend certificates. The judges considered their work extremely promising. If they continue to write and enter the competition, we hope to welcome some of them as prizewinners in years to come.

And this year's title for the book? It comes from Jack Camplin's poem, 'Drawing Pin', which gives a detailed description of how the head of a drawing pin distorts all that it reflects. Watching the stretching reflection of his hand in the drawing pin head, he observes, 'My hand is elastic.' The hand holding the pen or tapping the keyboard can stretch to embrace any subject, any form, any mood. In doing so, the writer reaches an audience far wider than an immediate circle of listeners.

Sir Simon Hornby
Chairman of the W H Smith Group

Advisory panel of judges: Ted Hughes, OBE, (Chairman), Michael Baldwin, Edward Blishen, Andrew Davies, Janni Howker, Jan Mark and Kit Wright.

Preliminary panel of judges: Lynn Barclay, Charlotte BrookeSmith, Richard Brookfield, Linda Hoare, Anna Hopewell, Barry Maybury, Richard Quarshie, Timothy Rogers, Betty Rosen, Professor Harold Rosen, Sheila Shannon and Tony Weeks-Pearson.

THERE IS IN ME A FIGHT THAT CANNOT STOP

Richard Joyce (17)

Jools Bailey (10)

There is in me

There is in me a red hot sun.
I have a bath to cool me off,
or I have a water fight:
We go in our swimsuits,
and Mum splashes us.

There is in me a fight
that cannot stop, and
I didn't start it!

Adam King (11)

Carlie Ayres (8)

Carlie

get up
hurry up
get down here
shut the door
that's my mum
stop talking
get on with your work
that's my teacher
give that to me
hurry up
that's my brother
one day I will
run away they will
be glad

*Richard Attfield (16)

I Fight to Have a Life

I am autistic. My difficulties are many. I will with words describe autism. I have myself sadly lived in fear of never communicating. Frightened always of words never speaking. If I words had myself been able to metaphorically speak. I found autism does not bring the words to my mouth. I words could actually understand and intellectually I longed to have communication. On the Canon Communicator I can now type and for the first time I can communicate with friends.

I never gave up hope that I would change and continue not to be autistic. I have tried. I will keep trying so I can have a life not one living with fear. I have lived with autism, lived with fear, I have had enough. I fear will certainly have but determination I have. The determination will get me through when fear does try to win. I want happiness. Why should I let autism win. I will fight autism for my happiness.

With awareness I write my experiences of life. Within I am the same as ordinary people. Other people do not see the you within. People do not realize my ability. I am the one who within realizes intelligent I am. No wonder understanding I never found when another non-autistic person could not relate to me. I feel touched when someone understands who I am. If I write about my problems people will understand and then given time autism will win no more. For freedom I fight to have a life.

I became aware words could give me life. Words are my friends. I am never autistic when I write. The challenge of writing has given me a life worth living. Words have found knowledge. I want freedom to find knowledge. I am knowledge eager to acquire. I believe words I will one day speak, then I will have a life to live and I will knowledge need to change my life. Weak muscles I have but I have not a weak someone inside myself. I will one day achieve what I aim for. I can acknowledge who I am. Autism never will control my life again. One life I have. I live knowing within the someone is free. One day everyone will know who I am not the person on the outside the one within.

Steven Pearce (8)

Steven vs the Garden

Steven Pearce comes round
the clothesline,
Over the rhubarb and through
the peat.
He passes to the dustbin but
the chair deflects to the
tree.
Steven Pearce wins it back
and the chair falls over.
His mum says play on.
He strikes.

It hits the shed and goes in
what a GOAL!!!!!!

Julian Ballester (10)

Anna Ballantyne (7)

Anna Ballantyne (7)

*Wheely

'Really it wisnae me!' said Mikey Ruelworth. He's one of the bad three brothers down the street. It's Mrs Keenwell, she's disabled and when she was going down the hill to the shops Mikey pushed her faster and she went wheeing down Loodyworth Street . . . but when Mrs Keenwell stopped with a jolt she did a somersault out of her wheelchair and landed on her back. Everyone in Loodyworth Street was around Mrs Keenwell, even Mikey was there. That was when Mikey said, 'It wisnae me!' The reason why I say it, was because I was just coming out of my house with the dogs, Tilly and Phoebe, and Mikey pushed her, but I was afraid to tell anyone or I would get the blame and I would get made fun of at school and Mikey would do horrid things to me.

The police were there and so was Inspector Toodlegood and he asked me if I'd seen anything. I never wanted to say anything but I thought it would be for the best so I told Mr Toodlegood and he did believe, but only for a minute because I started to laugh. Mr Toodlegood asked me what I was laughing at and I said, 'Because Mrs Keenwell is lying with her feet in the air and her knickers showing.' 'Oh, yes,' said Mr Toodlegood, 'get her into an ambulance and take her to the hospital.' Mikey Ruelworth finally admitted that it was him because too many people had seen him do it and were going to tell on him anyway. At school the next day Mikey put a frog in my desk and called me horrible names so I told the teacher and Mikey had to go to the headteacher and had to write 'Bad Mikey Ruelworth' a hundred times on the blackboard. When I got home the dogs ran up to me and gave me a lick. I go down with the dogs on Sundays to Mrs Keenwell's house to see how she is and I think she likes chatting to me.

Jools Bailey (10)

To

To hear the eclipse
as they join together,
to hear the curtains close
as people go to sleep.

To touch a strange wind
as it starts to go strong,
to hold a voice
that sings so lovely.

To taste a noisy thought
that types in my mind,
to taste a river rushing
down my throat.

To understand the girl
picking on me for nothing,
to understand where the lives go
when they are dead.

David Stallibrass (13)

My Religion

In my religion
My name shall not be used as an expletive.
I shall not be drawn as a sixty-year-old ghost on a death bed.
I won't live in the sky
Looking down on my minions like a crazed megalomaniac.
I'll do something on the seventh day
Instead of sleeping and taking root;
I might even do what I say,
Like save some people's lives,
Stop some wars (which I started in the first place),
Maybe even nudge my followers in the right direction.

I think I would be a far better god than the current despot.
What has he done since time began?
Nothing.
He sends us the Messiah,
Starts more wars
And pain
And suffering
Than you could imagine.
Then, like Stalin, declares it is all in the interest of peace.
After the small exertion of power he settles back,
Content that that will make him strong, and liked.
He settles back to have an eternal game of chess
With himself.

Daniel Storey (15)

Adrenalin

Three a.m., dark, cold and a full moon,
My board waxed,
My wet suit zipped,
I take a run and launch over a small wave
And skim out onto the silver ocean.

I wait, and then as the water rises behind me,
Paddle, paddle for the sand,
Faster, faster, until I can rise up on the board . . .

Now adrenalin rush,
Ride the wave of energy,
Slide to the left,
Shoot through the tube,
Get air,
Wave breaks,
Eat beach!

Tim Scott (15)

LEGENDS SCRATCHED IN THE SKY

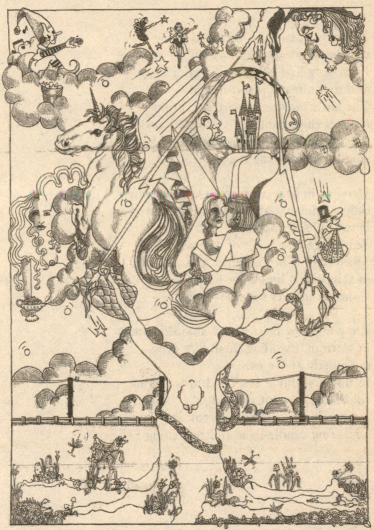

Josephine Robinson (15)

Rebecca Barr (15)

**Solstice

I'm lying outside on the hard stone
that backs me and knows me.
I can only half perceive the cool night
and that already is too much.
The air is moving toward something,
night perhaps: and the violet sky says 'Yes'.
Bats flicker past and cricketing birds
sing strange among the trees.

Here, as in heaven, there is no morning
only a knowing and beautiful pause
between light and shade and dark –
denying the meaning of any words.
Moth-light is not here yet and we wait
in thin-lipped limbo for nothing.
Cold air and yet summer–skies;

Knowing how the seasons abandon stars
in warmth, shedding them like eyes –
die quietly above us.
In this sky only a few hard fires glimmer:
cold Mars, distant as God,
shadowed Venus straining toward the moon.
Flickering candle-light and retreating hell.

The clouds are skimming through the air,
breathing out their limbs –
reforming themselves in their living.
Dripped candlewax green upon the sky
as the mountains collapse into black
and grey of mourning.
Whose death is this? Who watches
through leaves and the bleeding eye?
Sleep falls; lidding with green clots
my eyes from a falling eternity
and hiding my mind from this watchful night.

Louise Begbie (16)

15

Yolanda Barton (8)

Yolanda Barton (8)

Prophecy Girl

I sit on my pile of skins.
The dim light flickers,
And the flame of the animal-fat candle flickers.
Patches of light fall on the walls,
My stomach feels empty, painful.
I pray to the buffalo spirit
But there is no answer.
She does not tell me the hunters will return,
With food.
Wait! In the flickering light
My hungry eyes see a bison move.
I reach for my spear, and throw it.
It whistles through the air . . . and breaks on the wall.
This is not a bison but a lifeless cave-painting.
This painting was etched on the wall yesterday.
My eyes water, and my heavy body
Falls back on the pile of furs and skins.
Yet again the painting seems to move.
Then I see it!
The bison runs across the wall,
and a spear hits its side!
I leap up from my furs and the picture blurs.
I give a 'thank you' to
The mighty bison spirit
Whose strength is given to the hunters who kill his body.
He has given the omen unto me.
I shall bear it well for him.

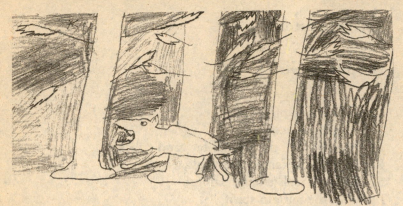

Philip Whitehead (9)   Nick Taylor (8)

*Night-time

Stars are Greek legends
scratched in the sky,
the moon, a dented
silver coin.

Night is the black hole
sucking the light in,
the wolf hunting
the shadows in the wood.

I trap it in my hands,
in my clothes;
it's in my stomach,
cold and damp.

It's under the stairs, and
when the letterbox chatters,
and the moth sneezes
in the lampshade.

Cara Bendon (6)

The Moon

It lives in a field, like a bull field.
Sometimes it flies through the sky
when it's being chased.
It wears a coat with white all over it,
and on top grey on both sides,
and black in the middle.
Its tummy is white.
It's silvery black and shiny,
you can't buy it.
Sometimes when it's worn out
of flying in the sky
it butts you like a goat.

Ifan Gwilym (6)

19

Llinos Roberts (12)

*Becoming an Owl

This is a poem about the transformation of Blodeuwedd into an Owl by Gwydion the Wizard. Blodeuwedd is a girl made from flowers in one of the Mabinogion stories.

Gwydion said the magic words,
And my flesh turned into feathers.
My head turned into a moon shape.
My shoulders squeezed into my body,
I was small and I felt trapped.

Feathers were sprouting all over my body.
It felt like pins being pulled from my pores.
My hands turned into sharp vicious claws,
My shoulders went heavy,
With the extra weight of wings.

On my back was a long tail
Which made my head pull back with the strain
My mouth was pulled down into a beak
I called out for help, but there was no voice
Only a ghostly shriek.

Now I was an Owl
The creature of death.

Maureen Hurst (11)

Erica Betton (8)

*The Gorgon's Head

One chop,
And it's off.
In the bag,
Hisses arise awake they are,
Off he goes.
Shows the head to the laughing
Crowd,
Turned to stone in an instant.

Emma Lawson (15)

*God Took a Dish-cloth
and Wrung Out the World

God took a dish-cloth and wrung out the world,
Sighing, he squeezed until tiny droplets oozed from every
   hidden pore,
like butterflies in a storm they swirled before landing in a
   heap on the ground.
Running his hefty fingers along the cloth, he moulded a great
   crease,
and then, rolling it into a fluid ball, pressed it into shape.
This, he said, was his land, and then looked down and smiled.

With careful carelessness he drowned his world by dipping
   it into a half full sink
and in the grooves appeared tiny rivers, moving rows of
   water
invading in tiny spurts, he watched them with pride.
And, as he said this was his sea, he again looked on and
   smiled.

Then God took the soap and smothering it in water
he beat it into a bubbling pulp before splitting it into
   hundreds of tiny pieces.
These, he said were his people, he placed them on top of his
   world,
but slowly, lifting his hand, he pulled out the plug,
and the water gurgled and screamed, his world became
   trapped in the hole,
and again he looked on and smiled.

Ysanne Friend (8)

Snow Baby

Where it's dark,
Where it's grey,
Where it's cold
A snow baby lay,
Crying in the snow, the deep, deep snow,
With icicles hanging off her fingers,
Stalactites and stalagmites,
Her body starts to linger.
Her dainty hands and feet are very frail,
And her thin, slim body very pale.
She lies in a crib made of ice and snow.
If I was her I would be frozen solid
But was she? – No.
When she grows up, she'll be a snow queen,
And wear a robe the colour of cream.
She'll ride on a sleigh made of sharpened ice,
She will be evil and not very nice.
Now she's just a baby with no power,
But soon power will fall from the sky
In a glitter and a shower.

Guy Lancaster (11)

*The Bag

Mrs Daniel's bag is a big bag, as big as you can get. The leather is tinged with age, the buckles try to shine but it's an unhappy dullish goldy grey. The bag gurgitates books and more books and more, night and day. Little bags of things lie idling about, some dozing, some fast asleep. The bag has no bottom and it's so cavernous that if you watch her out of lessons you might see her climb right in it looking for her glasses which are stranded on some lonely ledge in the depths. She has a pet monster which lives in the depths. It guards her bag day and night and bites intruders' hands. She feeds it every day with left over lunch and Nesquick. The monster likes abseiling down the rocky crags jumping from ledge to ledge. I really don't know how Mrs Daniel carries it around.

David Stallibrass (13)

Reincarnation

I once came back as a joke.
It was a good one too –
Made the recipient very rich,
It did.
That was just after my embodiment as an equation:
$E = MC^2$
Quite difficult to come to terms with,
What with Hiroshima and all that,
So I mucked around the void for a few decades.
Now I'm me,
Here.
Far more fun than being a weightless abstract.

Next time,
If I pass my aptitude test,
I'm going to be a deity.
I'm told it's fun,
With good job-satisfaction
And an excellent pay package.
Not much chance for promotion though
If you think about it.

Christian Miller (15)

Ten Astronomers

The first watcher
blissfully overzealous,
leaves warmth to watch
the constellations,
despite the bitter cold.

The second observer speaks in Algorithms
Altazimith and Ascension,
removed from Reality
as a bird's flight from earth.

The third gazer,
brings back picture-slides,
showing the rich hues of nebulae,
To impress the members of the Astronomy Club –
until he mislays them.

The fourth looker,
Speaks in similes of American origin,
excited by the universe becoming apparent,
experiments in ways, practical and humorous,

The fifth scrutinizer
at home in front of an audience
speaks in clear, precise tones,
Even when experiments misfire.

The sixth viewer
Is the eager office worker
who attends every lecture
with pride in going there
takes in very little
And comprehends even less.

The seventh,
is Organizer
follower of patterned lists
arranges trips to the Observatory
Then makes everybody tea,
carefully avoids questions about recent supernova.

The eighth
once a lecturer,
To him, the world's population
are undergrads,
worries about those people
whose astronomy knowledge is feeble
yearns for a bright student,
to help his mind stay alive.

The ninth
Speaks in quick enthusiastic bursts,
these interspersed
by queries to the effect of:
'Did anyone understand?'

And the tenth
Once a conservationist
Once an anthropologist
Once an astrophysicist,
But never, ever twice.

Zoë Redgrove (16)

**Orion

The Scorpio incident was rather a landmark –
the passing from ordinary, everyday Just Giant
to a stretched immortality – imagine your hands
light years from your elbows. Imagine
a whole orchestra scraping at their strings
every time you breathed out,
nebulae for your spiralled hair and
the Dog Star always at your ankle.
I was stung badly too, a jarring,
a sympathetic opening-up of doors into space.

Maybe I'm a forgotten Artemis.
I know every star in his body by name,
those half imagined arms picked out in light,
raised above his head
in a balancing act of war.
He spins across the sky, painfully slowly,
accompanied by the rages of hissing suns,
planets tearing and renewing.
He has to move so carefully, so cruelly,
because he is devoting all his energy
to getting into my Other Lands, those
cities behind my eyes.

He appears everywhere, in the chaos of water,
reflections in the window, abstracts in the wallpaper,
quieter now in the sky.
Sometimes he stands by every signpost
and tells me how many millennia to my destination.

Occasionally he hangs out of each tree in every forest,
one lazily long, elegantly bony foot pressed against the trunk,
fingers dangling, skeletal hooks, from amongst the leaves,
ready, if I reach out, to pull me high, higher
into the dust and darkness, the airlessness of the sky
where the unicorns and flying horses
are simply shafts of light.

TIME TRAVELS BACKWARDS

Max Naylor (14)

Nicholas Mathew (16)

**The Thrower

The day when I noticed the existence of the Thrower is very clear in my mind. It was during the summer holidays when a group of my friends from the laboratory took me to see one of his shows. Apparently, he was already quite renowned, and the show was part of a tour of the country; I think my friends considered him a bit of a joke, so we went to the show expecting to be able to laugh at the man.

The show took place on a wide playing field just outside of the city. Everyone sat down on the grass in the sun, and policemen made sure that there was a large patch of grass on which the Thrower could perform. I was surprised at how many people turned up to see him, my friends told me that he had quite a large cult following and, looking around, they seemed to consist mainly of rough-looking 'bikers' with leather jackets and large, worn boots.

The claim of the Thrower was that he could throw any object – large or small – further than anyone else in the world. At first, like my friends, I had considered this rather a ridiculous and pointless claim, and had expected to see a rather undramatic display from a man who liked chucking things around. But it was not like this at all.

The Thrower emerged from a tent that had been pitched by the clear patch of grass to roars from the crowd. He was tall and chunky, and he walked with an abnormally straight back, as though, underneath his worn leather jacket a plank had been inserted and tucked into the back of his worn jeans. His hair was tied back in a pony tail, and a long, drooping moustache gave his face the cool seriousness of a Hollywood film star.

Robert Pepper (15)

Basically, the show involved him throwing around an assortment of objects – including, among other things, a chair and a dictionary, and then members of the crowd began to hand him their own items to throw.

I was very impressed. It is difficult to describe, but the way in which he threw things seemed to make absolute biological sense. After years of studying the human body, I have to say that the way in which he manipulated its functions was perfect. With small objects, like a bunch of keys, he had a way of flicking his wrist and twisting his body which could send them surprising distances. With larger objects, he had a way of handling them which seemed to be 'correct' – as if he had solved a riddle as to how one threw anything – his hands would grasp different parts of an object which would enable him to catapult them incredibly far.

My friends left before the end of the show, but I stayed – my interest having been aroused. This allowed me to see the throw which amazed me and made me vow to follow the Thrower and to discover his secret; this was no ordinary 'strong man', he was a scientific genius.

I was just close enough to hear the Thrower's voice, a thin, human sound on the fairly silent field, not always recognizable as words. Suddenly, a motorbike tore a gangway through the seated crowd and stopped in front of the Thrower. The policeman had a short word with the biker who controlled it, before nodding and backing off.

The biker was a young man. He got off his bike like a cowboy dismounting his horse and took off his helmet, then he stood looking the Thrower in the eye with a peculiar stance, as if he was preparing to draw.

'Throw my bike, man.'

I doubt if it was his bike. It looked new and shiny and not what the biker should have taken pleasure in seeing thrown.

I think I saw the Thrower give a little chuckle before he looked disbelievingly at the young man.

'Throw my bike, man,' said the biker, slightly threateningly before backing away and putting his hands on his hips. The crowd was absolutely quiet, people towards the back began to get up in order to get a clearer view.

The Thrower looked thoughtful. He approached the bike a number of times as if about to pick it up, but backed off. Then, with an air of decision, he grasped the right handlebar with his right hand, and kneeling, he stretched round and grabbed the back wheel with his left hand. Suddenly, crying out with the effort, he hauled the motorcycle onto his shoulders and rested it on the back of his neck. He stood with his knees bent and his legs apart, with gritted teeth and screwed up eyes, shuddering under the strain.

Then, wheeling round with surprising speed, he spun the bike on his shoulders, and giving a great shout he released the motorbike, and it flew about twenty feet in the air, eventually landing with a crash, yards and yards away.

It was quite a finale, and the whole crowd went wild. But one thought occupied my mind – I would talk to the Thrower and learn about how he did it.

It was useless trying to see the Thrower after his performance. Not only was I one among many, but he must have been swept off long before anyone expected it. Nevertheless, I got a chance to speak to a man who was helping to pack up the tent. He was not a biker, he looked a bit like a student. He wore all denim: blue jeans with a denim jacket with the cuffs turned up. When I first approached him, he was kneeling by the guyropes with his back to me.

'Hey, you!' I called.

'No, he's gone.'

'Yes, I know he's gone.'

'What do you want, then?' asked the studentish man, impatiently.

'I need an address or telephone number to contact the Thrower; in person.' The blue denim man got up.

'He won't do adverts.'

'I don't want him to do an advert. I'm a scientist.' I had him with that one.

'Oh.' He knelt down again and turned back to the guy-rope. 'You don't look like a scientist,' he said. There was a pause while he fiddled with the guyropes to no apparent end.

'All right, look' – he stopped fiddling and turned back to me – 'I'll give you a number you can ring. Ring in the evening – nine or ten – and say Alan gave you the number.'

'Alan,' I repeated.

He gave me a card from his back pocket.

'We have to move on, the day after tomorrow, we're doing another show up north. If you want to see more throwing, you can see George Hedges next week, he's not very good, but people like him all the same.'

'There's a rival thrower?'

'Yeah. Quite new, though. Like I said, not as good. Hedges copies the real Thrower like mad – that's probably why he's doing the show near here. It's out in the country somewhere – a village green, I think. I've got a poster for it somewhere around.' He produced a little yellow poster for me, and I thanked him, taking it and the telephone number with me.

I was becoming obsessive about finding the Thrower. At first I mistook the feeling in me for a kind of hero worship, but my excitement ran deeper than that. My mind kicked over the possibilities of putting such a skill as the Thrower's to use. It was not purely chucking things around, it was having such a knowledge of one's own body in relation to the world around it that it gave him immense power. But how did the Thrower do it? Was it instinctive or calculated? Could it be learned?

I was full of such questions when I telephoned the number from my house the following evening. I was quite surprised when the call was answered, I did not think that it would be quite so simple as the man by the guyropes had made out.

'Hello?' it was a man who answered.

'Hello, I'm calling to speak to the Thrower. Oh, and Alan gave me the number.'

'Oh, he did, did he? Well, I'll see if he's here, who did you say you were?'

'I didn't say I was anyone. I'm a scientist.'

'Oh.' Then the man added as an irrelevant afterthought: 'He won't do adverts.'

'I know,' I replied, but he had already gone to seek out the Thrower from wherever he may have been. I couldn't help thinking what he may have been doing. Was he practising? Did he need to practise?

The phone was picked up again, a low, husky voice spoke. 'Yep?'

I introduced myself and told him that I was a scientist and very much interested in finding out about his technique of throwing.

'Why's that?'

'Because I believe the throwing as you do it is biologically fascinating in the sense that it requires the optimum knowledge of the interaction between the human body and objects around it.'

'Bullshit, I throw things.'

'Is that to say that your throws are not calculated, mathematically or otherwise?' I asked. My problem was that I was being far too technical.

'Why should I tell you how I do it?' said an annoyed Thrower who had been confused by my language or the motive behind it.

'Don't you think that your scientific knowledge should be shared?' I said, probably sounding annoyingly clever-clever. There was a long pause.

'Nope.'

That was that, I suppose. I never got another chance to speak to the Thrower, and I never tried again after making such a hash of the first interview. Instead, I thought that I would attempt to speak to the rival thrower, George Hedges, after his show the following week. Perhaps he would be more prepared to tell me about throwing than the actual Thrower – if I handled the interview well enough.

George Hedges' throwing show was held on the green of a village called Verges, about six miles from where the Thrower had performed. It was a very hot and sunny day, and the occasion had the atmosphere of family outings. Lots of mothers sat with children, eating homemade sandwiches, grinning at each other and squinting into the sun.

Everyone was so engrossed in their twee holiday pleasures that George Hedges' arrival was somewhat ignored except for a little weak applause from those not holding sandwiches.

George Hedges was a small and slight man in his late twenties. He wore an expensive-looking, eggshell-blue suit with a red tie and his short hair was combed into perfect neatness. His show was rather dull and, certainly, I must have been the only person who remained silent and attentive throughout. The largest thing he threw was a rather pretty Victorian hatstand – a bit of a waste, I thought. He was good with larger items like this, and he gave the same impression of correctness that the Thrower had given, but he was less impressive with small objects – which he threw rather like you or I would throw a cricket ball – only much further.

Hedges and his team departed straight after the show, and I failed in my efforts to speak with him, being too slow; but seeing more throwing gave me some material to do some calculations. I took notes on each of his throws, and I calculated roughly that the way in which he threw seemed to put all of the muscles in his body to maximum use. But what really bugged me is whether he had made these same calculations himself or whether he could just feel how to throw correctly. Are you born a thrower, or do you make yourself one?

For weeks I struggled to answer this by doing experiments which never worked – I even tried some throwing myself. I was overcome by the desire to know the Thrower's secret – I was drawn into a kind of madness by my ignorance.

I remember with embarrassment a time when, after hurling my ironing-board as far as I could in the park, I was approached by an old lady with a small rat-like dog who looked up into my face over her little glasses and said:

'What *are* you doing, my young man?' to which I sat down and burst into tears.

I thought that I had lost track of the Thrower and might never discover his secret. I was at a complete loss as to what to do, my experiments had failed and I had run out of ideas. I needed to find the Thrower or Hedges again.

I was utterly overjoyed, then, when an incredible piece of luck came my way. Pinned up in the window of a newsagent's in the city was a poster that caught my eye. It advertised the 'ultimate meeting' between what was described as 'the two big throwers'. George Hedges had challenged the Thrower to a contest of throwing.

The venue was to be a farm which was about fifteen miles away. It was to be held in two days' time, so I immediately began preparing for it. I took a new piece of equipment with me that I had bought solely with the intent of using it on such an occasion. It was a special camera which took two frames every second at the touch of a button. With this, I would be able to capture the secret of the Thrower on film and record his every move.

The day of the meeting came. I drove to the farm along the winding country roads. There were a lot of motorbikes on the roads that day, sometimes in convoys, and almost all of them were on their way to see the Thrower and George Hedges. The sun had decided not to shine on the event – the sky was an even grey right up to the horizon. As I drove, my heart beat fast with excitement, my mind was constantly exaggerating the importance of the throwers. What power would I have if I discovered their secret?

At the farm, groups of people – mainly bikers – were seated on the banks of a large river tributary. A few acres of short, tufty grass was put aside for the contest; policemen stood at different points all around it, and along a pretty wooden bridge that crossed the tributary.

While I set up my camera, the crowd grew larger and larger until half of the field was covered with leather clad bikers and a whole pack of motorcycles parked close together in one corner.

In the middle of the bare patch of field was a big tent, and I focused my camera on it, while also including the rest of the field in the shot, so as to be able to register the distances that objects may be thrown.

Then, to deafening cheers, the Thrower and George Hedges emerged from the tent together. Hedges was wearing a cream-coloured suit that day, with a black shirt buttoned right up to the neck without a tie. The Thrower was wearing his usual leather jacket, jeans and a white T-shirt. He nodded at the crowd as if he was some kind of deity – it was hard and yet so easy to believe that this was the man who had spoken so tritely to me on the telephone.

My hands were sweating with excitement as I poised my finger above the button of the camera and the crowd quietened. The blue denim man poked his head out from the tent. Everyone was silent now. I felt like a Buddhist who was on the verge of enlightenment. Hedges stretched out his hand for the Thrower to shake, and the Thrower took it.

I still have the twelve pictures that my camera took that day. I had looked at them many times after they were developed, but I never used them for experiments or anything, of course.

I came across them in a drawer just the other day. They were not in the right order and the first frame that caught my eye was one of the Thrower.

His eyes are wide and staring, his mouth is hanging open in a look of surprise and horror. His hair is falling this way and that about his face. I had caught him in mid-flight. The next shot was of his landing. The little bridge is splintering like matchwood against the Thrower's back. His hands are screwed up into fists and his legs are pedalling the air frantically. The leg of a policeman sticks up comically from the tributary while another policeman has just made impact with the water and has scrunched up his face; the water splays out around his limbs, which are stretched out straight all around him. The crowd are calm and have not quite yet realized what has happened. Some of them are still looking over at Hedges, who is squinting at the Thrower with his hand shading his eyes.

I was surprised that the crowd did not attack Hedges at the time – most of them ran over to find the Thrower. The police got to Hedges before the crowd could, and he is in prison now, serving an eight-year sentence. The Thrower was buried in Italy according to the local paper; his name was John Donizetti and his father was from Florence.

I find it strange now, that I attached so much importance to that particular sport of throwing. At the time, I thought that endless possibilities were open to a scientist who had the same skills as the Thrower. Now, I am not so sure – in fact I do not really care. Nevertheless, it will remain an unsolved mystery as to quite how throwing was done before the day when the Thrower was thrown.

Laurence Corns (13)

Death of a Hare

The hare, a prince among animals,
Now wears his crown of flies.
Barely alive, the hare stays alert.
A twitch of his nose registers change.
But a flicker of his limbs fades
Before the dead shell of his body moves
And the swarm rises,
Disturbed by my presence,
Unclogging ash-coloured eyes
Which stare upwards like two pale moons.
Dignified in death,
The hare's form loses none of its grace,
Long ears pointed
Like two sentries at the palace gate.
He will see two sunsets tonight,

One shining over dark hills and dusty meadows,
The other lighting up the lush grass of pastures new.
As the black-blue flies descend once more,
The hare appears suspended,
Neither dead nor alive
Lost somewhere beyond my gaze
Mirrors through mirrors.
Time travels backwards
Towards the beginning of all life
At the moment of death.

Daniel Sedgwick (11)

*Snail in Hunstanton

The snail, as innocent
as the Birmingham Six,
has come out to damp itself in the rain
and we
the giants on the school trip
have walked down to the dark beach
with anoraks and wellies.
I am the unlucky one
to step on it.
I look back and see it there dead.
I feel hot salty tears
stinging my eyes.
Carl (one of us) cracks a joke
about three men
but all I can think about
is the snail.

Anjali Joseph (15)

A Summery Winter Day

It was one of those cold, bright winter days. The sun burst fitfully out of the clouds. Inside, where it wasn't windy, it was hot, even summery. Jonathan Season sat in a deckchair on the middle of the dusty third-floor room, watching with pleasure the light through the slowly falling dust. Closing his eyes, he could feel it *was* summer . . . without effort images of the green, grassy school field with lazy, basking children all over it, sitting in a boat on the river – the various icons of summer began to float into his mind.

In the almond tree below the window, fluffy with premature blossom, for it was not yet March, he heard some chirping. The room door opened slightly as the cat came padding in. He rubbed around Jonathan's feet, then flopped suddenly and comically on his back in the sunshine.

Jonathan thought about last summer. It was a little like watching a film about someone else. He couldn't connect his last summer's self who sat in the deckchair now, couldn't connect that person to reality. It hadn't all started in summer, but in summer came the part he remembered best.

It had been July when they found the body in the canal, with the brilliant sunshine on it. Jonathan was the first one to see it there, floating, grotesquely puffed up, the face horribly purple. He hadn't thought of it as a face, belonging to a person; it seemed like a mask, suspended theatrically in the water. He'd wanted to laugh. Time seemed to have stopped. When Claire saw it she looked at it meditatively, *watched* it, as if trying to understand in a very literal sense why it was there. Tony, the last one to see it – he was at the front of the boat with his back to it, rowing – said 'Oh God', in revulsion. Jonathan and Claire both turned to him and gave him very peculiar stares, like a pair of biologists, whose prize mutant growth has just been described as disgusting.

'We'd better go to the police station,' Tony said.

'It'll be quicker walking,' Jonathan said.

'Right.' Tony began to paddle them back and towards the side of the level canal bank. He stood up unsteadily and stepped out of the boat, bending it to hold it against the bank so that Jonathan and Claire could get out. The three of them stood on the edge of the bank.

'Right,' Tony said again. He turned and began to walk towards the bridge two or three miles upstream where the river went through a park. The police station was fifteen minutes' walk from there. Jonathan followed him.

'Wait a minute,' Claire said. Both of them stopped and looked around. She was still standing by the boat. 'Hadn't one of us better stay?' she pointed out. 'To make sure it isn't disturbed? And there's the boat.'

Jonathan looked at the boat and, beyond it, the long blur of the body, the face of which he could not now see. He felt like a child whose friends relentlessly play tricks on him, emphasizing his separation from their group. All he wanted was to turn around and walk away. But he felt that the question was directed at him.

'I'll stay,' he said.

'Are you sure?' Tony asked.

'Really. I don't mind,' Jonathan said reasonably. He avoided looking at the body, as if it might expose his cowardice, and sat down near the boat, settling the debate.

'Right,' Tony said for the third time. 'Well—'

'We won't be long,' Claire said. The two of them began to walk off, a little distance between them.

Jonathan watched them, indistinct against the sun, until, some minutes later, they rounded a bend and were out of view. For a little while he continued to face the direction in which they had gone, unwilling to look at the body. However, he couldn't avoid thinking about it and he began to imagine it being towed away quietly, through the backwaters by someone with a boathook . . . imagined the killer returning to check it was still hidden, and finding Jonathan there, killing him too . . . imagined the body waking, pulling itself noiselessly from the water, slipping up behind Jonathan and putting its puffed, slimy hands around his neck . . .

At this point he turned quickly around, realizing with relief that it was still passively floating a yard or two from the boat. After that he sat cross-legged, watching it, staring into the shadows of the trees on the left bank of the river, where it was dark. He suddenly felt enormously hungry. His stomach rumbled shamingly loudly, while his mouth was dry.

He wondered what would happen if some more people came around the bend of the river in a boat, and saw the thing and Jonathan near it. What he was doing there would, he realized, be unreasonably difficult to explain.

Fortunately as the minutes passed agonizingly slowly, no other boat appeared. But neither did Tony and Claire with the police. Where were they? He looked at his watch. The strap was sticky on his wrist. It was almost a quarter past one. What were they *doing*? They had left almost forty-five minutes ago – they must have reached the police station. Suddenly he thought: oh no, what if they don't believe us and don't come? Help!

Slowly the sun grew weaker. Eventually, almost an hour and a half after they had left, he heard voices coming around the bend. Three policemen, followed by two men with a stretcher and another with a camera. In the middle of this business-like group, Tony and Claire, looking excited if insignificant.

As they reached him one of the policemen said, 'Is this the other one?'

Claire said, 'That's Jonathan.'

Jonathan got to his feet. The photographer began to take

pictures of the body. After he had finished the two stretcher men pulled the body out, dripping. He had a vague feeling that one of the policemen was asking him something but the overriding memory was of the dank, too-ripe smell. It caught in his throat and turned his empty stomach, and he had vomited hopelessly over the grass.

Sitting in his deckchair in the sunshine, Jonathan could remember the whole day. He remembered the questioning that followed, the evidence he gave at the later inquest, the reports in the local newspaper. He remembered too that the murderer had never been found. They never knew who the body was.

And, as the new summer was slowly approaching, he still couldn't get rid of this absurd idea that one day there would be a knock at the door, and he'd open it to see a man wearing dripping clothes, a man with a bruised-looking, discoloured face and puffy hands.

Marilyn Rust (14)

Dear Mummy

She lay
In her elaborate coffin
At the Hancock Museum.

I hated to see her . . .
Me staring at her.
And she, staring back
Through blind eyes.

Her face was brown and
  shrivelled,
Like an over-ripe potato
On the verge of mould.
Her mouth was screwed up,
Lips tightly pressed together
As though she had just bitten
Into the bitterest lemon.

Her hair, black as jet.
I was amazed she still had hair!
It looked coarse, dry.
I imagined it felt
Like wisps of steel wool.

Marilyn Rust (14)

Her nails were embedded
Into her rusty fingers.
Her skin was brown
And tarnished,
Like old shoe leather,
Sticking to her ribs.
Arms and legs were withered
Like dying bean stalks.

When you die, you escape time.
But,
Here she is, still a prisoner,
Her body still confined
To Earth.

They say they're going to build up her face,
See what she really looked like.
Maybe she was an Egyptian Queen,
Cleopatra,
Nefertiti.
Maybe she will look like me!

But hasn't she aged well.

Stacey Hunt (14)

*His Beginning and His End

His face was red
Though he was not angry,
His face was wrinkled
Though he was not old,
His mouth was opened
Though he was not crying.

His fists were clenched
Though he was not fighting,
His body was puckered
Though he was not bathed,
His skin was bruised
Though he was not beaten.

His back was hunched
Though he was not crippled,
His legs were bowed
Though he was not paralysed,
His toes were curled
Though he was not scared.

He was born
Though he was not alive,
He was human
Though he was not normal,
He was named
Though he was not called.

He was stillborn.

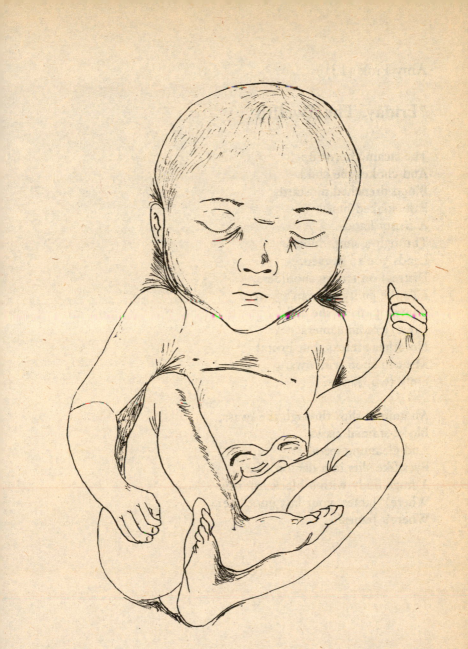

Stacey Hunt (14)

Amy Pink (13)

*Friday, The Twelfth

The steam churns up
And chokes the child.
Blood drenched mustard,
Pain soaked blue.
A trusty hand
Through a shop door,
Leads you to heaven.
Distress on strong shoulders,
Fills the guilty woman's heart.
'James, James?' she calls.
Gone, candid camera.
No other attacks, but brutal.
Meat in shop windows.
Only two, James?

An animal slips through the grass,
Blood-stained claws
And gleaming teeth.
Eyes like slits in a demon's face.
A huge body with a black interior.
Where's James, your last goodbye?
Where's James?

Now the morning's black
And the house is dim.
She curls up on a chair
And sleeps.
Last night was hell,
She could not cry,
She tried to sleep,
Yet when eyes closed
He appeared,
Her face not there.
The room was filled with toys,
And his un-made bed.
James, come home.

Amy Pink (13)

Carla Boylan (10)

When My Baby Cousin Died

It was on a Sunday afternoon it was absolutely silent as usual. I could only hear the wood crackling in the fire, I could hear the sounds of the water pipes bursting to break through, I could hear the sounds of my two brothers fighting and they are really big sounds, I can assure you. Suddenly the phone rang, me and Mummy dived to get it but she had arrived first. So I sat down in a huff again. Mummy walked in slowly, she looked upset. She called the boys down to have a talk. I knew there was something wrong because we only talked when there was something wrong. Mummy said in a hurt voice, 'Your baby cousin died.' We all said at the same time, 'What baby cousin?' Mum answered, 'Olive and Michael had a baby girl they called it Teresa but unfortunately it was too weak and helpless to live any longer.' My face went pale. I never even got to see her and I didn't even know she was born. I thought of her small tiny fingers and her little blue eyes twinkling in the light. I thought of her parents longing for a child. And now she's gone.

Joanne Mildenhall (15)

*A Sense of Place: Goodbye

I remember how we named the little pools of water that collected in the hollows where the roots of the trees made ridges in the soil, like the veins on my Grandad's hands. The names ring clearly in my memory after five years; ten years. I can't remember how long it has been. We made a song out of the names, Alan and I. We used to chant it as we swung from the ropes attached to the 'fire tree'. The swinging and the chanting had a definitive rhythm that I always seem to find myself humming when I look across the fields of Holly Hill. I laugh when I think of the words: the names of our 'lakes' in the tree roots: Blackpool, Liverpool, Hartlepool and Bath! There was also one called liaison manager, but that was a long story. It seems sad to look back now, and remember the wood. We used to swing from a rope attached to the 'fire tree', so called because we used to set light to the farmers' fields and sit in the tree so we could see the fireman come. It was a stupid thing to do, but we didn't know that then. I just remember the rope. It was thick, and had a knot at the bottom. It must have been there a long time, for the hands of a thousand children had made it shine in the middle, a smooth, polished segment in a line of coarse rope. I still have the scars where the rope made calluses on my hands . . . an imprint of memories.

The path was sloping. Once I had gotten down it I had trouble getting up. My dad was flying his glider. Alan was picking blackberries. I was bored. The grassy bank was soft. I sat down. I remember there being a patch of uncovered ground, where somebody had lit a fire. I used to find old cigarette ends and pull them apart until I found the nice fluffy piece in the middle. I used to take them to that patch and arrange them there like a line of clouds in the sky. I pretended that the patch was where the fairies gathered at dusk, and that they used my bits of cigarettes for their beds. I really believed it.

Beyond the patch was a stream. The water was clear, and Alan and I used to play 'pooh sticks' over the bridge there. The bridge was worn, and about three metres from the surface of the water. We used to swing our legs as we sat on the bridge and watched the bubbling brook weave its way through to the 'undiscovered island', as we called it. Later I discovered it was the road junction. Once I lost my jelly shoe, and it went floating happily off down the stream, minding its own business, a noble shoe! I never saw that shoe again. Alan said it had died and gone to heaven. I believed him. We held a funeral at the fairy patch. Alan planted a lolly stick in the ground, with 'died at sea' written on it.

Dad gave us his pen-knife once. We carved our initials on a tree: the one with liaison manager in its roots. The initials are still there: J.E.M., A.R.M. It looked stupid, but those were our initials. Our initials, together on the tree forever, the orange of the wood behind the bark showing the letters quite clearly in the shadowy wood. A path led past the 'lakes' and off into the shady glades. There were places where the path split to go around a tree, and I remember spending ages deciding which one to take. When we finally got to the glade we used to have picnics there: picnics of blackberries. There were thousands of them, all along the banks. Big, juicy blackberries, not like the ones found by roads. When Dad had finished flying the glider, he would give us an ice-cream tub and take us to get the blackberries for the cheesecakes Mum made us.

This place we called 'the slope'. We must have been about five or seven years old, Alan and I. The slope was Holly Hill. It overlooked fields where, if you looked closely, you could see the lines of the old strips used for farming before enclosure came. It was like a scar on the land. The hill was big, and the vista of fields and trees is implanted in my brain, like a negative, like an elusive brightness in the corner of my eye from looking at the sun too long. I remember the birds Alan used to watch from the trees; we were fond of climbing trees. Once up there, we would watch the leaves, blowing ever so slightly, the cool breezes moving the branches in a small dance. Alan used to say the breeze blew our thoughts to heaven.

I knew every path, every nook and cranny. I suppose I still do. There was a lady who came to the slope with her husband, flew his glider there. She was an artist, and used to draw me pictures of rabbits. The hill was like a cheese, with lots of holes in hidden places, waiting to be trodden in.

To the left of the stream was a large hole where a bomb had been. There was a rope, worn from the same hands that had worn the other rope. It was dangerous, but we didn't care. As we swung, the tops of trees, growing in the bottom of the crater, brushed our legs as they brushed the wings of passing birds. Devil's Hole, we called it. It was where I broke my wrist, and it was where Alan broke his neck. I remember people screaming, and the ambulance coming, but they were all too late, and it seemed to be the end of any affection I had for those woods.

It was eight years later when we finally returned to the hill. It was weird. The brook bubbled as it wound its way through the dark woods to the 'undiscovered island'. I sat on the bridge and watched the river go by. I watched the birds circle upwards with the gliders on the thermal. I watched the rope, still attached to the fire tree, swing in the breeze as if some child was still swinging on it, chanting as the leaves rustled in the wind that blew our thoughts to heaven. Nothing had changed and everything had changed: my sense of place had changed.

The bank was damp with dew. I could see the white flicks

of rabbits' tails here and there in the undergrowth. The people I used to see on the slope were gone, replaced by younger people. They didn't look as if they belonged in the place. As I walked along the track, I noticed there were more patches of uncovered ground: more places for the fairies to meet. The smell of the woods was there: a smell not dissimilar to that of chestnuts roasting on a fire, and also not dissimilar to the smells of summer flowers, like the ones I used to pick for my mother. It is a smell hard to describe. It is unending, and sort of tedious, as if it wants to go, but can't; as if it has been there for thousands of years, and would be there for thousands of years still, and as if it knows that, and is unperturbed, in a bed of thorns.

The initials, carved in time, still there. Their chestnut colour faded. They look old now. I suppose they are old. They move up the tree every time I see them, or they seem to. Liaison manager lies still in the dusky, gloomy place that was once dancing with light beams and rhythms; melodies of nature. Now the place had changed. But I realized as I unearthed the lollystick: 'died at sea', that it wasn't the place that had changed: it was me.

A man shouted something and another man shouted something back as we drove away from the slope. The sights and smells, and the rustling of leaves; whirring of glider mechanisms were laid to rest with the memories of a place I love and a place I hate, and the initials on the tree said it: goodbye.

Angela Heap (12)

The Blessing

When it came, it was a blessing, an angel,
Disguised as a mocking, grimacing gargoyle.
He was ill and
Its grip was not so icy after all.
It took him,
Stole him from behind our backs
When we weren't looking.
I didn't get to say goodbye.
I prayed it would be gentle.
It was.
It shook off pain's hold and released him.

Kate Levinger (14)

foot
steps
in The
Grass

YOU'RE THE FOOTSTEPS
IN THE GRASS

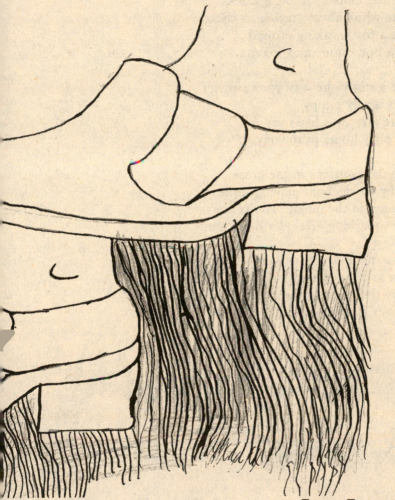

Emma Freeman (12)

Lauren Coffey (9)

*Barry

You're the monkey in our games,
the one who's always trying to cheat.
You're a fox sneaking around
to do a Boo on me and Joanna.

You're a storm the way you're rough
and a friendly puppy.
You are grey eyes like mist
in the early hours of the day.

You're the footsteps in the grass
made by an elephant playing 'follow
the leader' in the jungle. You're the
mouse squeaking around a hard sum.

You are the distance between
the fox and the clawing rabbit.
You are the moment the shadow
casts over the playground.

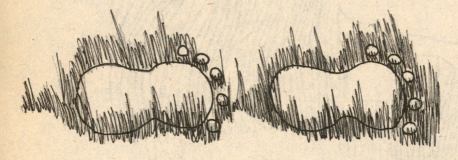

Emma Flaxman (12)

Barry Turrell (9)

*Lauren

You're a new daisy
that's come up at night,
your skin is
a silk cover rubbed
against my hand.

You're a moon
drifting through frozen air,
the lady who helps me
when I'm hurt. You are
cream just whipped.

You're a red lipped flower,
the bit of butter
melting on my potato,
you're the hot water in my
bath, rushing around me.

You are god talking
quietly to horses,
a rainbow in the sky.
You're the moment
I get my sums right.

Carla Boylan (10)

My Grandad

My granda is about six foot four he has a round tummy and he has a very loud happy laugh. He is a widower, my granny died recently he is very lost without her.

Mummy told me about the time Granda came home from work he walked through the front door and Granny bumped into him and the pipe went down his throat he never spoke to anyone for two weeks.

I like my granda very much he is a kind happy man and I wouldn't let anyone hurt him. Ever since Granny he just sits looking at her photograph.

He holds his feelings in. I now can feel the loss of Granny and I know Granda does too. And I love him.

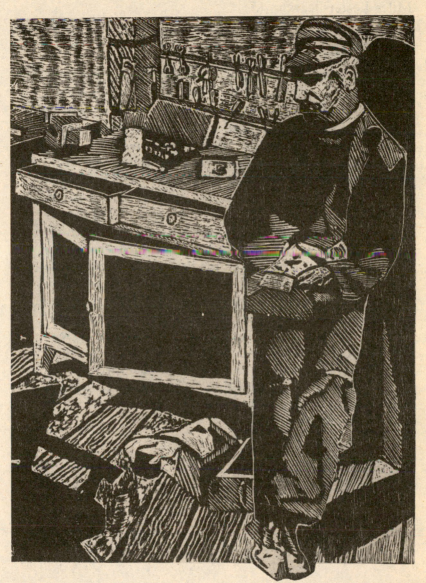

Tom Arthur (14)

Miles Lester-Pearson (5)

*My Dad

My dad has a car to go to work. One day I was making a runway out of Lego and I told my mum to tell my dad to come and look at it. My dad asked me did I want to go to work with him to see the *Yorkshire Evening Press* office. I didn't want to go because I was playing with my Lego. Then I said, 'I will come with you, Daddy.' And then I just ran to the coathangers and put my coat on. Then I ran to my dad and he opened the car door. My dad turned the key and the car went *brum*. It was very hot in the car. Then we went to the sticky bun shop and got two cherry buns, one for Georgie and one for me. At the *Press* Daddy went up the stairs with me, then we went to see the papers being printed. We saw the printer. He was dressed in blue trousers and blue shirt. He has to press buttons. The buttons tell you what happens to the machine. The doors are secret at the *Press*. The first one went up and went *whirrr* then we walked through and it went down *eeeeeoooooo*. Then I went home. When I grow up I will turn into a daddy then I'll have to drink beer and wear a suit and carry a briefcase and I will work at the *Evening Press*.

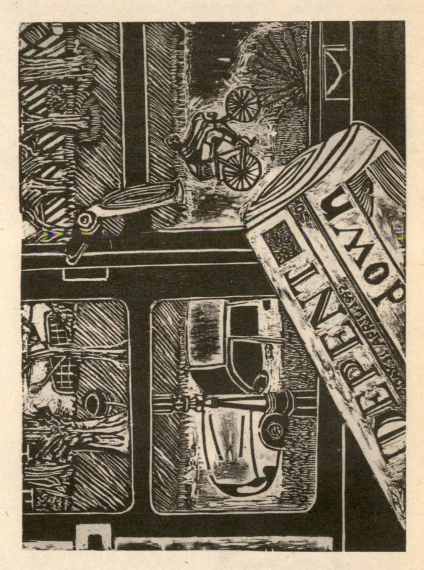

Scott Malpas (16)

Anna Ballantyne (7)

*Faces

Nose like mouldy bread,
furry stuff. Hair, hair, hair
everywhere, furry mouldy frizzy stuff.
Bald head-cold in winter
Hair sticking up everywhere,
Ladies with beards, sore when you kiss them,
Men that don't shave, sore when you kiss them –
that's when Gillette comes in handy.
Makes you think of Popeye's girlfriend,
all petite and funny.

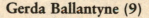

Gerda Ballantyne (9)

Thin, drawn faces – not like mine,
you won't be drawn to me.
Guess who has all the faces; fat, skinny.
I guess some have hats – silly ones,
Some make you look like an Eskimo
but the ones from Moscow, you can't beat them.
Saint Bernard dogs, floppy things, when they shake,
oh no better watch out the saliva's coming to you.
Perfect faces thank goodness for that.
No squint nose or anything, just one little beauty spot.

Anna Ballantyne (7)

Zoë Sorkin (14)

The Watcher

Hetty Bryant watched the girls in the playground. She sat in the same place every breaktime, on the stone steps by the swings, doing the same thing: watching. She watched Apple talking and the other girls laughing (of course, thought Hetty viciously, they would have to laugh at 'Madam's' jokes) and Tory running after Primrose, and Violet and Emmy arguing about a waterfight (trust *Violet* thought Hetty; I bet she cheated) and, with some interest, the first years picking bits off a tree. It was all wonderful – but . . . Why, thought Hetty, why on *earth* can't I go and join in? Why shouldn't I? Why shouldn't I just run down these steps, and pull Madam's hair and say, 'Oh God, Apple, are you *still* telling your stupid boring jokes?' Because, of course, one didn't *do* that sort of thing to Apple Peasey. But I could join in. They'd always let me. I *could* join in, but I never will. Suddenly, Hetty was aware of footsteps behind her, and spun round a second before Violet drenched her with water from a plastic cup. Hetty fled. *That bloody Violet Vicars*, she thought fiercely as tears dripped down and mingled with the water from the cup.

I cry too much, Hetty told herself, as she came full circle around the playground. Not that it matters. She settled herself on a grass bank and loosened her black hair from its vivid blue band. This scrunchy, Hetty pondered idly, is a statement: a rebel, a demonstration against black hair and brown uniform. It's not a Hetty; it's an Apple. Oh. If only, if *only* I was Apple's best friend. I don't care if she's bossy and unfair and a Madam. If I was her best friend I wouldn't ever have to watch again. It was a hopeless wish of course. Apple was Celie's best friend, and adored her. Celie was

70

Charlotte Ashby (14)

another statement, very like the blue scrunchy. She was beautiful and good and very slightly mad, and it was obvious, perhaps not to the world, but certainly to the watcher, that Apple was fonder of Celie than Celie was of her. This was the basis of the hope that was the last hold on Hetty's wish, and Hetty's wish was the only thing that kept her a watcher, and the only way she could hope to stop being one. Suddenly interrupting Hetty's reflections, came the bell. It went every day at exactly the same time, like a contrary cockerel, crowing for the living world to immerse itself in the sleepy safety of lessons. Hetty watched the girls troop inside, still laughing and talking and then when the last girl had limped around the corner (Agnes Pellet, mused Hetty, is *such* a hypochondriac), Hetty jumped down from her grassy perch, and followed.

Inside the schoolhouse, Hetty lingered outside the classroom door, watching the class until frustration overcame habit, and she *had* to hear what the girls were saying. She sat on the lockers, watching, and hoped no one would notice her. What a show-off Apple was, and how *very* devoted to Celie. Hetty watched, growing more and more involved in the dramas around her. Agnes was such an idiot. It was a miracle Martini put up with it. Oh! Hetty gasped – Limey Ricetti had thumped, actually *thumped*, Agnes on the head. Agnes was bound to 'faint' again now. But no – she was actually retaliating . . .

'Why don't you ever talk to anyone?' Hetty grimaced. It was Primrose, Limey's best friend. What did she mean? How could anyone reply to a question like that?

'Because I don't feel like it.' (What a stupid thing to say.)

'Why do you always watch?'

'Because I like to.' (I've never told such lies.)

'Oh.' And the second bell went.

Hetty Bryant watched the girls in the playground. She sat in the same place, every breaktime, watching. But today, there was no excitement in it, no fun. Suddenly Hetty Bryant stood up. Then she did something she had never done before. She took slow, deliberate steps, down to the playground and right into the middle of the crowd.

'Oh God, Apple,' she said clearly and distinctly, in a voice that had never before been known to speak above a murmur, and was now tinged with mingled amusement and malice, 'are you *still* telling your stupid boring jokes?'

Emma Harvey (12)

Heard Yet Not Seen

Why me? I don't understand! Emily stared blankly at the world beyond the window. It was like a television screen, transmitting to her what she was missing, and would always miss. The image became blurred and she drew her arm over her eyes soaking up the tears on her sleeve. There was a knock on the door; Emily tensed and replaced her feelings with a false smile. 'Come in.' The door was opened and her mother's patronizing look fell onto Emily. 'Darling, I was wondering whether you would like to sit outside. It's such nice weather.' Emily nodded, her expression was one that she used to completely smother her inner self.

Her chair was positioned on the lawn facing towards the city and Emily gazed wistfully at what lay before her. It was the same view as that from her bedroom window, yet it seemed different with the soundtrack. Suddenly her thoughts were disturbed as Muffin bounded into view. Emily laughed at this spectacular entrance from her beloved border collie and reached for a stick that lay beside her chair. It lay just out of reach and she distantly apologized to Muffin for her useless legs. Muffin raised his head and looked at her. She smiled; it was ridiculous to feel such self-pity. Muffin seemed to understand and curled up by her feet, using them as a pillow.

'My darling.'

Emily turned her head to look at the source of the sympathy.

'I'm sorry, but Miss Reeves has just rung inviting us to tea. I told her that if you weren't up to it . . .'

'Mum, that's fine.'

'Oh, and Miss Reeves was keen for Muffin to join us.'

Emily smiled meekly. She could imagine the conversation that took place. Miss Reeves would have missed her name out of the invitation, but her mum would have gently persuaded her to have Emily as well, that poor girl of twelve who was involved in an accident, and now has to spend the rest of her life in a wheelchair. That was the trouble, everyone assumed that since her legs were not working, her mind was at a halt as well. No one seemed to understand how she felt; they all gave her constant pampering and sympathy, yet Emily needed encouraging and she desperately wanted to be treated and talked to as twelve-year-olds are. To Emily her one companion who would always understand was Muffin.

Cedar Cottage looked immaculate even from the outside. The lawn had perfect stripes of grass, and this was bordered by rows of flowers that always seemed to be in full bloom. There were two large oaks towering over this array of beauty, yet in all Emily's visits to and from Cedar Cottage, never once did she see the tree one would have expected to see, a cedar. Miss Reeves was an amazing person, she played a main part in village life while at the same time managing to keep her house and garden in immaculate condition.

Emily swung from car to wheelchair, and began to wheel

herself up to the door. Her Mum intercepted and began to take over by pushing. Emily just wished that her mother would let her get on with her life or Emily would become as helpless as everyone thought she was.

The doorbell rang and Emily was pushed into the house with Muffin wagging his tail as he often did in a new environment. Miss Reeves stood tall and proper and showed the way to the dining room. Muffin was seated on a rug, Emily next to him, Mum and Miss Reeves sat opposite.

Miss Reeves smiled sweetly. It came over as rather false although anyone with such a tight bun could not have done much better. She turned to Muffin continuing to smile.

'Muffin, would you like a drink of water? Yes, I thought so.' She turned back. 'Heather, does Emily want some orange juice?'

Emily stared at the floor and her Mum fidgeted, and then answered, 'Yes.'

Miss Reeves then struck up a conversation about herbal tea.

Emily forced back her tears, wondering how anyone could humiliate her like that. It was as though Emily was some kind of foolish species whereas Muffin was thought of as an intelligent being. She knew Miss Reeves was slightly short-sighted but could not imagine it possible to mix up a dog with a human being.

Emily slowly sipped at her juice, still staring at the floor. She could hear slurps coming from Muffin gulping down his water. The conversation was at a halt and Emily's mother was looking anxiously at her daughter. 'Beatrice, I don't suppose Emily could go and explore?'

Miss Reeves glanced at Emily. 'That's fine.'

Emily detected a note of nervousness in her voice and looked up. 'Thank you, Miss Reeves.' Emily switched from chair to wheelchair and departed. She could feel two pairs of eyes following her to the door. She opened it and entered the sitting room. Her eyes fell immediately on the tall bookcase to the right of the door and she turned to face it. The books varied from well-known novels to books on how to look after your garden. Emily picked out a book of poetry and flicked through. She used to get top marks for poetry in school before the accident and her so-called 'rest from work'. Emily read a few and was very impressed. She looked at the title. *John Betjeman's Collected Poems*. The door opened and Emily's mother stood in the doorway.

'Emily dear, it's time for us to be heading home now.'

Emily carefully replaced the book and wheeled herself for a while until her mother took over.

Muffin bounded out of the front door and just missed a headlong collision with a tree. Emily chuckled to herself; he was such an innocent comedian. Emily got into the car and when the journey was underway she took the opportunity to ask about the poet John Betjeman. Emily had of course heard of him but until then she had never read any of his work.

'Mum, do you know anything about the poet John Betjeman?'

Her mother looked awkward before saying, 'He's definitely a good poet, and he . . . he . . . has Parkinson's disease and is condemned to a wheelchair.'

Emily stared out at the countryside that seemed to be a blurred mass. This news came as a shock to her. At last she could relate to someone, someone who understood.

Emily was wheeled into her position by the window, she opened a nearby drawer and took out a file. When opened, it revealed a whole collection of poems that Emily had recently composed. She was interrupted by a bell indicating that supper was nearly ready, so carefully placing the file back in the drawer she wheeled herself to the hall where her mother took over.

Emily sat at the dinner table. Her mother kept looking at her watch and asking thin air when her husband would be home. The front door opened and in rushed a rather windswept man who instantly began to apologize for his lateness. His wife, who did not take in a word that he was saying, began to dish out portions of the cold food.

'Hello, my darling, how are you feeling?'

Emily glanced up at her father's drawn face. 'Fine thank you, Dad.'

Emily's mother sat down with them and her parents began to talk. Emily noticed that her dad had become completely invisible due to a rather large flowerpot containing a plant that had been placed in the centre of the table. Emily smiled as her mother looked ridiculous striking up a conversation with a hyacinth.

Emily ate her food slowly and every now and then contributed to the conversation. Her father began to talk about an arts festival that was held every year. Emily remembered that a friend of hers entered last year. It was held in the nearby city and the winners from each section would win a sum of money and something else that her father couldn't remember. Emily enquired about which arts would be involved.

'Err . . . drama, music, poetry . . .' Emily distantly heard her father finish the list, yet she was already planning the poem that she was to enter.

Bursting with ideas she rushed through her meal, and excused herself hurrying off to her bedroom where she began to write. She scribbled away, excited by the prospect of the competition, she found it an exciting challenge and was determined to put in her very best work. After a while Emily put her pen down and read through her poem. She corrected a few spelling mistakes and read it again. It was a poem that expressed the deepest feelings she had experienced in the recent months, and how she became exasperated with the way she was treated. Emily was satisfied with her work and decided that the most likely place for her to find the address to send it to was in the local newspaper.

Emily scoured the pages searching for the address. At last she found it and copied it down onto an envelope in which she put her poem. 'Mum, are we going to go down to the post office stores at all today?'

'I wouldn't mind popping down: I need some eggs and mushrooms.' Emily was pleased with this news as she could buy a stamp and post the entry.

Emily wheeled herself into the post office and her mother began choosing the groceries she was getting and Emily went over to the post-office counter.

'One first class stamp, please,' said Emily in her most polite manner. The lady tore off one and Emily gave her the money. Outside the shop was a post box fitted into the wall. Emily remembered that when she was younger, she always used to think that there was a huge pit behind the friendly looking exterior and that strange creatures lived there. She posted the letter and wheeled back into the shop.

'Emily, what were you thinking of, going out of the shop without me to help. There's a road, right outside, and goodness knows what could have happened.'

Emily could feel herself growing red as other customers turned to watch the spectacle. Her mother finished her lectures and Emily was wheeled out of the shop. Emily felt as though she was a baby being pushed along in a pram after having a telling-off in front of what seemed like a crowd.

The next week was a dismal one as Muffin was taken ill and had to stay for the whole week at the vet's. Emily missed him terribly and felt at a loose end the entire week. Saturday came and it was that evening that Emily's father was to collect Muffin from the vet's. It was supper time and Emily waited at the table, her senses at the ready for Muffin's return. A key was turned in the door and Muffin bounded over to his beloved mistress. He jumped up onto her lap and she hugged him fondly. Emily noticed a bald patch on Muffin's left side where he had had the operation. He looked rather strange but Emily's father reassured her that the fur would grow back quickly.

They all sat down at the table, and the radio was turned on ready for the local weather forecast. The food was served out and they began eating although Muffin was bouncing about so much that they all had to watch their food carefully.

'Hello, this is your local radio station and in a few minutes we bring you the weather, but first the results of the local arts festival.' Emily froze and her heart leapt into her mouth. 'In the drama section Lucy Hufton came first and she will be collecting her fifty pounds at the award ceremony next week, congratulations, Lucy. In the poetry section the first prize winner is Emily Marshel and she will be collecting her prize of fifty pounds at the award ceremony next week as well. Congratulations, Emily . . .' The voice drifted away and Emily slowly lifted her head. Her parents both dropped their cutlery and stared at their daughter. Her father continued to stare and her mother slowly got up and walked round to Emily. Emily looked into her mother's eyes, and her mother looked back. 'Emily, I had no idea. Oh, Emily.'

Her mother bent down and they hugged. Emily could not hold back her emotions any more and she burst into a flood of tears. 'I love you both so much,' she said in between tears. 'My darling,' said her father who had joined Emily as well. They all hugged each other, each one of them letting out all the bottled up stress that had been collected. Muffin poked his nose through her parents' arms and they all laughed, a thing that they had not done together for a very long time.

David Jones (12)

*The Wound

The wound seems small
to others, a mere scratch
caused by a name, just small,
but truer than you think.

But to the owner it's deep
and sore. It sticks around,
it deepens and gets much worse
than a cut finger that heals quickly.

But this sort never heals.
No matter how hard you try,
it never quite leaves
completely, it bruises.

It bruises deep and stays
there hurting. All the time
it's there, black and blue.
And just a slip of the tongue
can open it again.

Emma McCarthy (14)

Rebecca Barr (15)

**88 Malone Road

I could live here quietly alone,
in my room of frozen light
with warm imaginings and soft air
to float between my thoughts
and the moving lips, to speak gentle.
I could open my window to the
sad rain and green heavy leaves:
for that would be feeling too,
but removed from this time,
suspended in equilibrious eternity.
It would be different from feeling now.
The seasons would move and turn
around my window; circling me,
centring me – the quiet omphalos.
They could put food inside the door
when I didn't see them and pause
from the merciful unnoticing of life.
Still air to comfort me when I wake
to the softly sleeping silence
and the moving light outside.

Solitude.
Without thought.

For I could live here quietly alone,
with opened books and pencils for my devils:
pages to haunt me no more.
Everything to die after first love,
except I who am without.
The dying tissue cell to bulge
and hold me in its quiet greyness;
its vacancy forgotten.
My hollow head denoting sagacity
denied and crossed forever –
my forgiveness died with love.
But if I lay in my forever, here,
the restless wave of haunting despair
would drown me in my pointlessness.
The nightmare's shadow grow,
concrete itself – re-inforce
the motives, gain its ground.
The distant thunder disappear,
storm fall and I could never know
or share the living.
No, I cannot lie and observe,
for impartiality cannot resolve.
The entire nothing would be a crime
to all that I loved.
But it was love that drew
me here – to empty city streets,
dolorous suburbia, flatliner
of this century. Suffocating
its dead babies in the back room –
pray to wriggle out alive.

Anjali Joseph (15)

Looking for the Cow

Luke looked at the gentle, concerned face of his teacher.

'What's the matter?' asked Mr Andrews. 'You've been skipping your English lessons,' he pointed out, 'and you haven't been doing any work. This GCSE coursework isn't just going to do itself, you know! This is your final year, Luke. Why all this now?'

Luke could see the man getting frustrated and angry. The gentleness was beginning to fall from him. He was suddenly incensed by the teacher's supreme arrogance. What he really wanted was for Luke to come up with something obvious so that he could trot out a few of his trusty nuggets of advice and solve all Luke's problems. He probably imagined ending the fatherly chat with a firm hand on Luke's shoulder and an injunction to, 'Come back if you ever need to talk,' followed by grateful stammered words of thanks from Luke. Luke looked at the teacher with fresh eyes. Until now he had not disliked him.

'Well? Answer me!' demanded Mr Andrews with noticeably less patience.

All desire to be honest or straightforward left Luke. He felt so disgusted with the man that he couldn't bear to give him any of his miserable satisfaction.

'Oh, well, you know, sir,' he said smoothly, leaning back in the chair and folding his arms in a leisurely way, 'just boredom, really.'

The foolish face of the Schoolboy's Friend darkened. He looked very angry indeed. He said in quite a nasty voice, 'Look here, Followes, I think I'll be writing to your father, see what he thinks about all of this, hmm? I really don't like your tone. I think your father will have something to say about this insolence.' His voice assumed a more confiding tone again. 'You're only making life more difficult for him, you know,' he said.

'Yes,' Luke agreed politely. 'Well, if that's all, sir, I think I might go and finish my prep.' He got up and walked to the door. As his hand was on the door-knob the teacher said, 'Oh, Followes.'

'Sir?'

'You're really not as clever as you think, you know.'

'Sir,' said Luke, closing the door after him and grinning because he'd won, for the time being. He bounced down the corridor, jogged down the circular stairs and trotted into his study in the West Wing. He nearly tripped over the large feet of his room mate Stuart. Stuart was lying out-stretched on the floor. He seemed to have fallen asleep unintentionally – there was half a lit cigarette in his left hand which made a worm of ash on the carpet, and a paperback copy of *Macbeth* lay by his other side. Luke, who disliked untidiness, put out the cigarette, scooped up the ash and put the *Macbeth* on Stuart's desk.

He sat on his bed for a little while, looking around the room; the bookshelf, filled with his books and Stuart's *Viz* annuals; the Metallica posters above Stuart's desk; the burgundy velveteen curtains and, above his bed, Luke's only poster. A huge six feet in area, it showed a scene from *The Lord of the Rings*, Luke's favourite book, painted in the best swirly watercolour style, and complete with mists, a dark shadow and hordes of orcs. He was sorry he couldn't take it with him, but it hardly mattered – he knew it by heart.

Stuart started to snore and reminded Luke that he had to go. He reached under the bed and pulled out a neatly packed rucksack. Then, drawing the curtains, he quickly stripped off his uniform and changed into his jeans, checked shirt and sweatshirt and trainers – black school shoes being a dead giveaway. Finally he jammed his fat, one volume paperback edition of *The Lord of the Rings* into the rucksack and walked out of school, doing a half circuit of the sports field before hopping over the fence behind the cricket nets.

It was amazingly easy, that was what he couldn't get over. He had planned it for weeks, and it came off perfectly. Feeling suddenly exhilarated, Luke made for the railway station, where he was just in time to catch the 7.47 to Wool (his ticket having been bought a week previously).

The carriage was empty and as the April light faded Luke began to feel a bit self-conscious. Rather than reading his book, he found himself running over a conversation he'd had with Bill before Christmas. Bill had been reading this book, *A Long Journey*? No, *The Longest Journey*, that was it. Luke put his feet up on the seat opposite his. In the book, there was an argument between two characters. One of them said that nothing was real unless you could see it. He said, this character, that if, for example, you were in a field with a cow, the cow was there as long as you were – once you went it ceased to exist. Luke, who was not of a philosophical bent, thought that in terms of reality it was a pretty stupid argument, although he had to admit that it was thought-provoking. What if you shut your eyes? Would the cow still be there? And if the cow wasn't there, surely neither were the field nor the sky, the sun or anything else. What about reality for blind people? Did the impressions gained from other senses count as real? Luke gave himself a wry grin. He sensed he might have lost sight of the point somewhere along this line of thought.

There was another facet to the argument, which one of the characters comes up with, which is that *some* things (for instance the cow) really exist, and some things we just imagine. For the thousandth time Luke wondered why the argument fascinated him so much. Perhaps it was because he had so often thought that the world around him was largely unreal, although life at a public school, he supposed, was not exactly representative of 'real life'.

This, then, was more or less what he was looking for; why he was, at nearly eight o'clock at night, several miles from where he was supposed to be: a sense of reality. That, and partly an increasing feeling of having finished anything he might possibly have had to do at school. He realized that he would have to go back for the exams, well before them in fact. But he wasn't looking ahead that far. Right now all he wanted was—

The train stopped. Peering through the window Luke read the station sign, just to check. It was Wool, and he picked himself and the rucksack up and stepped off. The station was dark as Luke walked through the waiting room to the front. A maroon London cab was waiting. Luke asked how much it would be to Lulworth Cove, and was told about seven pounds, maybe a little less. He agreed and the taxi was soon trundling along the small roads, bordered by bulky hedgerows. Luke just leant back in the comfy, cushioned interior of the cab and relaxed. When the cab stopped in front of the small bed and breakfast Luke had named, he felt he could have happily taken a much longer ride. It certainly didn't feel like a £6.77 journey, he thought rather ruefully as he fished in the pocket for change.

'I'm sorry, I've only got £6.54 in change,' he told the driver.

'That's all right,' said the man comfortably, somewhat to Luke's surprise.

'Er, thank you very much,' he said.

'You'll be coming back in a week or so then?' inquired the driver.

'Well, I'm not sure when . . .' Luke said cagily.

The driver handed him a business card. In the murk Luke saw it had a phone number on it in bold red letters, as well as a name and slogan he couldn't read.

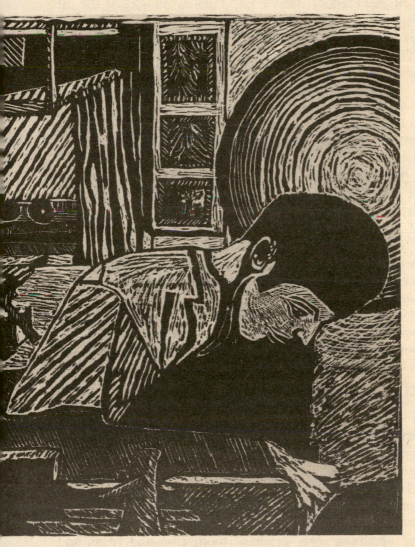

Nick Bayly (15)

'You give us a ring the day before you want the taxi,' the driver said.

'Right, I will. Thanks a lot.' Luke stood back as the cab went off down the road, turned into the gravel car park nearby and came up the road and past him again.

Then he walked up the steps to The Cove B & B, Hot and Cold, Television Lounge, Full English Breakfast.

A fat, curly-haired woman opened the door.

'Hello, can I help you?' she said in what Luke guessed to be the first Dorset accent he'd heard.

'Yes, I'd like a single room, please,' he said, and was invited in.

'How many nights will you be staying, sir?' inquired the fat lady – by the name of Mrs Evans ('My husband was Welsh') – as Luke signed the register as Mark Lucas of 27 Tunbridge Road, London.

'Just one, thanks,' said Luke, feeling a little thoughtful. He was shown to his room and told that breakfast was served at eight-thirty and lasted for an hour. Check out time was ten-thirty.

Shutting the door as the fat lady thumped rhythmically down the stairs, Luke dumped his rucksack on the bed. The room was decorated in average bed and breakfast style, with pink frilly curtains, a brownish carpet and dressing-table and matching chest-of-drawers in white chipboard. Luke sat down on the bed and took off his shoes and socks. He moved two fluffy pink towels from the foot of the bed to the back of the dressing-table chair, and stripped and folded the towelled, be-fringed synthetic counterpane (of a pea-green colour), which he put on top of the chest of drawers.

He opened the rucksack, removing soap, toothbrush and toothpaste, hairbrush, comb, nail file and pyjamas. He put the file on the dressing table with the brush and comb, gathered up towel, soap, pyjamas, toothbrush and paste, and went to have a very long bath.

When Luke returned he was cleaner and more cheerful. He had a happy facility for putting unpleasant things to the back of his mind, which he was now exercising. He wasn't running away, he was taking a holiday. He knew it wasn't true, that it wasn't real, but for now reality was on hold. He got into bed and switched the light off.

When Luke woke up it was, from habit, at a quarter to seven. Light shone from under the heavy curtains. It was cold and Luke stayed in bed for over half an hour. Eventually he got up and took his soap and towel to the bathroom for a quick wash. He didn't need to shave – he still only needed to about once a week, and it was only a light fluff then.

Luke dressed and carefully combed and brushed his hair. Then he sat on the bed and filed his nails. (At school – where cleanliness was, on the whole, thought to be wet – this generally drew a hoot from the two or three boys hanging around the study to talk to Stuart.) When Luke had finished his grooming he put away the various tools employed and went down to breakfast.

The fat lady was down, in the kitchen. She spotted Luke as he came into the dining room and said good morning cheerfully.

'What would you like for breakfast? Cereal? And some sausages? Eggs? Bacon?' she offered.

Luke settled on cereal followed by two sausages, with coffee and orange juice. The cereal was Coco Pops, which he crunched through happily, and the sausages came with mushrooms and fried bread. When Luke finished the coffee he took the plate and cup into the kitchen.

'Um. I've finished. It was very nice, thank you,' he added politely.

'You're welcome, dear. You don't eat much, do you? No wonder you're so thin,' said the fat lady cheerfully – she seemed in fact incapable of being anything less than cheerful. For some reason Luke didn't find this irritating at all – it seemed to stem from a great store of optimism rather than from any smug self-satisfaction.

'It's a nice day today, isn't it?' he ventured.

'Lovely,' agreed Mrs Evans. 'What are you going to do today?' she asked.

Luke wondered. 'I think I'll walk along the coast for a bit. Then in the evening I have to go and see some friends in Dorchester. I'm catching the train,' he told her.

'Lovely,' said the fat old lady. 'Would you like some sandwiches, if you're going to be out most of the day?'

'Er, oh yes, that would be wonderful, thank you,' Luke said with some surprise. He looked at his watch. It was a quarter to nine. 'I should be leaving in half an hour or so, if that's all right?'

'Just call me when you're ready, dear,' said the fat lady placidly. Luke went upstairs to pack.

Roughly half an hour later he stood at the door of the room with his rucksack packed. He felt quite sorry to leave it, pink though it was – it was also comfortable, friendly and nicely impersonal. It didn't belong to the Luke Followes of school or even the Luke of home; in fact it didn't belong to anyone. No connections, no reminders, no guilt . . . He shut the door, taking the key down with him. Mrs Evans was already in the dining room.

'There's your bill, fifteen pounds including VAT,' she said.

Luke produced the cash and signed the bill.

'Oh! I almost forgot your sandwiches,' said the fat lady, returning to the kitchen. She came back with a brown paper bag.

'How much do I owe for them?' asked Luke.

'Nothing, dear. They're all made out of bits and pieces,' she added as Luke protested.

Mrs Evans saw Luke to the door and he walked down the

steps of the house and down the small, sloping road to the cove.

The sun was very bright as Luke walked down a small concrete ramp onto the pebble beach of the cove, a perfectly oval shape. The sea was very blue and a few boats were moored in the water which was clear as the sun shone through it. The beach shelved into a basin and the chalk cliff was a brilliant white in the sunshine. Outside the cove mouth the sea was infinite. The possibilities for the day seemed endless as Luke sat down on the pebbles, a yard or two from some over-turned skiffs and not far from the edge of the sparkling water.

He sat there for a long time, watching the sun and the water. Peace descended. The water had been blue since the start of time, and after Luke had gone, it would still be there, and the sun . . .

He fell asleep, head on the rucksack, for a little over an hour and a half. When he woke, face to the sky, he remembered the taxi. He had to phone the taxi. He stayed for a little while, trying to convince himself that he need not go, that he wasn't responsible for the school, that the cow wasn't there.

But, but, but . . . But what about Dad? The school might have phoned him by now. What about his lessons, his exams? He wondered absently if it would be too late to phone the taxi – the driver had said, 'phone the day before,' and it was not one o'clock. Anyway Wool was only five miles away; he could walk if he had to.

He walked up the road and took the short path up to the cliff top. When he got to the top he ate his sandwiches and took a last look at the sea through the 10p telescope at the edge. The sky clouded over. Luke sighed and began to walk down the path towards the phone box at the end of the road. It wasn't summer yet and it was suddenly chill. Reality – who needed it?

ALL MIXED UP

Emma Cole (7)

Joanne Mildenhall (15)

*Friends

A solitary car moved slowly along a highway. The highway led to Smyrna, Georgia. The car was covered in dust. It had English registration plates. The air was heavy. The car stopped. From the back seats climbed two small girls, one fair, one dark. The dark girl ran towards the side of the road. The fair girl followed her. They knelt down in the dust. Two dark-haired adults got slowly out of the front seats of the car and turned to watch the girls play.

The dark-haired girl drew a fish with her finger in the sand. The fair girl watched her disinterestedly, and started to fidget. The dark girl watched her as she rose and wandered along the side of the road. She got up, brushed the dust from her knees and walked over to her friend. The fair girl turned. Her friend crinkled her brow and stared at her: 'I was showing you something.' The fair girl muttered something. The dark girl waved her arm at her: 'Well, what do you want to play?' The fair girl scuffed her shoe up and down on the dusty road. Finally, she shrugged. Her friend frowned, 'Well, come on then,' and pulled her over to the drawing of the fish in the cracked earth.

Four bright yellow balls lay scattered over the steaming green surface of a tennis court in a small Kentish village. At the head of the court was a veranda. On the seat sat two girls, teenagers, one dark, one fair. The dark girl was staring at the sheep in a distant field, squinting because of the bright sun. The fair girl picked at the strings of her tennis racket impatiently. She spoke: 'So how are you?'

'OK. How are you?'

'Good.' The fair girl looked sidelong at the dark girl, but she was staring into the air, as if mesmerized by the heat.

The fair girl looked at her watch and sighed as if she wanted to be somewhere else, or anywhere other than where she was. She looked away across the green recreation ground and sighed again. Then she looked at her friend. 'I just got a brace on my teeth like Amanda's.' The dark girl turned and looked at her.

'Yeah . . .' She stared at the fair girl, as if she had just realized something important that had been eluding her. The fair girl looked down at her tennis-racket cover on the seat beside her. She waved an arm towards the bikes parked by the entrance to the court and looked at the floor.

'I've really gotta go . . . I said to Amanda I'd go to her house.'

The dark girl looked intently at her, as if searching for something. Then she stared at the bicycles, turned her head and once again looked lost in the heat. The fair girl shuffled her feet. The netting of the tennis court and the trees the other side of the veranda made opposing patterns on the wooden boards they sat on. A cool breeze blew. 'I'll be going then.' Not a question, thought her friend, just a statement. She didn't move. 'Bye,' said the fair girl, jumping off the veranda. She got her bike and rode off over the green recreation ground holding her tennis racket in her hand. The dark girl turned her head to look at her but somehow her glance missed, and she ended up staring at the trees.

She always had a camera in her hand, as if frantically cataloguing each moment so it wouldn't escape her. She had a whole collection of sunsets. They meant nothing to her.

In the summer evenings she would drag a chair to the end of the garden and sit there, sometimes reading, sometimes writing and let the wind play with her hair, until the sun went down.

She closed the curtains during the day and opened them at night. Often, if she could not sleep, she would go down to the end of her garden and watch the stars. The stars enchanted her. She believed she actually heard them shine sometimes, when the night was clear. You don't hear things, she thought, until you listen, or are silenced by those who don't. That was what she believed – she believed she had turned loneliness into beauty.

She went to school by herself, came home by herself. She spent her time looking to the future, as she believed there was nothing in the past she had not properly lamented.

But she was OK. She had passed through many stages and played out many parts, each time walking off one stage only to find another. And she had found a part she liked – the part without an audience; the play on which light is never shed – the red velvet curtain hung still.

And life went on. She believed she had done her time for earlier sins. She believed others would pay for theirs too – she believed life was fair. And she was OK.

The bus that took her home was small. She paid the driver and stepped over the luggage to a seat at the back. The bus moved down the road.

At the next stop stood four people. The bus stopped. Some people got off before the others got on. Luggage was removed from the aisle, shopping bags from seats, coats from luggage racks. The scene of the bus had changed.

She watched the fair girl step onto the bus, not knowing what to do. A quiet, desperate tension twisted inside her. She felt like pushing her off and driving off to somewhere safer. The fair girl paid. As she watched her sit down their eyes met. She turned away, but the damage was done. The scene of her life had changed, and she knew there must have been something she had forgotten – something she had left behind. A part of her was missing. Even though the girl had not spoken to her for five years, she still had something that belonged to her. She owed her that. Still. But what could she take?

The light from the stars clarified her thoughts. She lay on the grass looking at them, into them, around them. She believed they were thoughts. They were thoughts to guide you if you were lost – to show you the way. And then she knew where she had to go – she knew the road to take.

In a room in a house in a small Kentish village sat a girl. Her dark hair made patterns on her white shirt. She put a compact disc into her stereo and lay back on her bed. No thoughts crossed her mind. The music washed over her. It filled her body until she was just a thought – just one thought. She listened intensely to the voices, unravelling the melodies and finally understanding them. Consciousness eluded her.

A solitary car moved slowly along a highway. The highway led to Athens, Georgia. The car was covered in dust. The air was heavy. The car stopped a short way from a group of small children playing in the dust of a lay-by. A young dark-haired woman got out of the car. She had a large bottle of water in her hand. As she leant back against the car she took a sip from the bottle, just enough to wet her lips. A car rushed past on the road, bringing a cloud of dust up and over the car. The woman turned to look at the car moving off into the distance. It vanished into a haze of heat. She turned her head to look at the children playing. There were three boys, all dark, and two girls, one dark, one fair. She walked over to them slowly. They were drawing pictures in the sandy dust. She stood over them. They took no notice, absorbed in their game.

The woman held the bottle of water over the drawing the fair girl had made and tilted it until the drawing was swimming in a mess of wet, sandy mud. The fair girl began to protest loudly.

Quietly and slowly, the woman reached into the back pocket of her jeans and slid out a black revolver. She pointed it at the fair girl. Slowly, calmly, she pulled back on the trigger. The fair girl fell into a puddle of wet sand and blood. The woman gently smiled, slid the gun back into her pocket, turned, got into her car and drove off into the heat to somewhere safer having turned loneliness into beauty into death. I was right, she thought – life is fair.

Gerda Ballantyne (9)

All Mixed Up

It was Saturday and Mum was taking me to the Zoo with her new fiancé, I never knew how to feel. I remembered just last year it was Mum, Dad and me at the Zoo but now things have changed. Mum and Dad had a divorce after being married for eleven years. I stay with my dad in a cottage in a small village, and the only time I see my mum is at the weekend. I wish Mum and Dad would get back together again, but I don't think that will ever happen because Mum doesn't love Dad and Dad doesn't like me seeing her at all, not even when he has me most of the time. I was thinking all of this when the doorbell rang, I knew it would be Mum but since I had been crying a lot I ran to the toilet to try and cover up my red eyes. Dad answered and invited Mum and her fiancé (called Mike) in and told her I wouldn't be a minute. Most of the redness of my eyes had gone but they were a bit pink now. I walked into the room and ran over to Mum and gave her a big hug then I looked at Mike but I never gave him a hug because I felt worried if Dad wouldn't like me and feel jealous so I just said hello. Mum got my coat on even though I could do it myself because I am seven! Then we were off in the car. It was quite a long journey in

Gerda Ballantyne (9)

the car but I couldn't wait to see the animals. I was happy when we got there because I knew Mum still loved me even though she never loved Dad, but I was sad because I wished it were Dad and Mum taking me and not Mum and another guy who I hardly knew. We went to see the lions and tigers first and watched them eating their dinner. The man who told you about them said they were eating dead lambs but they eat things like zebras, gazelles, buffaloes and lots of other animals. That put me off them a bit. Next we went to see the wolves, zebras, camels, elephants and giraffes. I was exhausted so Mike ran over to the ice-cream van and bought three Cornettos, which was a treat because they are seventy pence each. We all sat at a bench and ate our ices. We made our way just in time to see the penguin parade. As they were getting near us one of the ones in front (a penguin that is) came up to me and tried to eat my dress, but Mum quickly lifted me up and chased the penguin on. Thinking of it in the car on the way home it seemed quite funny, that and the jokes Mike told us. The red bottomed monkeys were funny, you could see them from the swing-park there. Then I thought of the big ape that sat in the window all on its own with only a few bits of wood to play on day after day. It must not know what it did to deserve being in that terrible small place. It felt like me, what did I do to ruin Mum and Dad's marriage. It's not fair on me, tell me a way I can sort it out and I will, I promise. On the way home Mum cuddled me in the back seat. I thought, I need a mum and a dad, that was how it was meant to be. When I got back to Dad's bit I said goodbye to Mum and gave her a hug and a kiss then I gave Mike a cuddle too. Me and Dad stood and waved at the door till the car was out of sight, then I looked up at Dad and asked, 'Why did you and Mum split up?' He said, 'We weren't right for each other,' then I thought, I will never make my children go through what I am going through. With that me and my dad walked in and shut the door.

Christian Miller (15)

Know the Sport: Being a Teenager

Introduction

Being a teenager can be a fascinating and educational way to infuriate your parents, and the sport is growing fast. Despite the daunting complexity of the sport when first encountered let me say, once you have mastered technique, very little talent is actually required – anyone can master this form of recreation with sufficient (or lack of) effort.

It is best to pick a reasonable age to start this hobby. Ages suggested by the author are between eleven and seventeen, with the optimum age being about fourteen/fifteen. Ages in excess of seventeen are not useful, as society frowns upon teenagers of ages eighteen and up, except in the United States, where people are more tolerant of older teenagers (enthusiasts of thirty-two years old have been recorded).

I will explain the state-of-the-art techniques, classic styles, favourite equipment, suitable quirks and popular behavioural problems of the youth of today, in detailed, but easy-to-follow sections.

Equipment

A certain amount of ambiguity is present when choosing equipment, but there are well-defined guidelines (as laid down at the 1987 JAC (Juvenile Annual Convention) meeting. You will, as a bare minimum, require these objects:

A bedroom

. . . /

A stereo/television/computer (any number of these options may be selected)

Furnishings (drawers, bed, roof, etc.)

Cosmetics and hygiene equipment (including, if required, comb, deodorant, styling mousse, gel, etc.)

Any other equipment as you see fit.

Step One: Attitude and Behaviour

When being a Teenager there is one Golden Rule to observe:

ACT STRANGELY

This is again ambiguous. Acting strangely entails acting in a way that is not 'normal' while toning it down enough not to be committed to a mental hospital (which would mean you having to persuade the nurses and doctors that you should be released – not an advisable scenario). So, while this particular area is great for freestyle performance and personal expression, stick to the classical styles for now:

Style a)   Introverted. Disappear into your room and ignore everyone. Talk to no one. Be interested in nothing – at least nothing anyone else is interested in. If anyone asks you anything tell them to go away. If you think you are rude, miserable and generally rotten, choose this style.

Style b)   Extrovert. The exact opposite to style a. Talk to everyone and anyone. Be interested in what everyone else is interested in and give them the impression you know everything about it – whether you know anything about it or not. Go to any party you're invited to, and gatecrash the ones you haven't been. Have a wild time, and make sure any friends you make will be exactly the wrong sort of people your parents think you should be going around with. If you are annoyingly gregarious, brash and badly dressed, go for this.

Style c) Egocentric. You have the mind of Albert Einstein, the sporting talent of the England teams for everything all rolled together, and are the best looking person in the entire school. At least that's what you think. Believe it hard enough and everyone will have to accept you as the most perfect human being ever. If it annoys people tell them you understand their feelings of inadequacy. Keep yourself scrupulously well-groomed and never comb your hair less than 9.9×10 exp 12 times a day (this is not limited to teenagers only – see Know the Sport: Being an Adult, for details on this style of play).

Style d) Morbidity. Practise saying 'I want to die' and 'Humanity is a disease on the face of the world' and other related statements. Lose faith in everything (the existence of God, the Spirit of Humanity, the existence of New York, etc.) and sit in your room reading French philosophy about the futility of existence. You can talk to people, but make sure to depress them. Life is a sit-com, it is unfunny and lasts too long. Excellent if you've ever wanted to wear black a lot.

Style e) Hypochondria. Agonize to everyone about your spots, your level of development, etc. This style surprises no one, but it is useful for an entry-level method of Teenagerization.

Style f) Insanity. Go round the bend, friend – or at least try. Good one for grabbing attention, this. Experiment with different psychoses – be either psychopathic, schizoid, schizo-phrenic, kleptomaniac (with care), paranoid, hysteric, luna-tic, or roll them all together (noooooo . . .). Note you are not actually mad, just pretending – don't let the teachers know you're acting this way, or you'll be in a strait-jacket before you can say, 'Ships? (Waargh, Gibber, Gibber) I see no ships.'

When you have chosen your style, proceed to the next chap-ter – it only gets simpler.

Step Two: Hobbies

When you're a teenager, hobbies very much depend on your playing style – consult the paragraphs below:

Introverts As noted before, be interested in anything, so long as no one else is into it.

Extroverts The exact opposite – be into what the crowd likes, and make sure you've done all of it, watched all of it, listened to all of it – etc. After a while you'll start leading the crowd – which is exactly what is supposed to happen.

Egocentrics Similar to Extroverts, but make sure that you know more than everyone else – and then some. Actually try to understand obscure things, like the closing scenes of *2001, A Space Odyssey* – and if you don't, lie about it. If you have enough loud, overbearing confidence, you can easily fool people into believing you.

Morbids Read lots of philosophy and wear black clothing – nothing else to say really.

Hypochondriacs   Make it your business to read medical dictionaries, and spend many happy hours poring over the NHS issued health leaflets.

Psychotics-Psychopaths   You know what to watch and read – but don't forget to describe all the gory bits in lavish detail to the poor fool who sits next to you in Science.

Schizoids and Schizophrenics   Nurture many different interests, but if one interest doesn't 'gel' with your parents' shrug and say, can't have been me.

Kleptomaniacs   Should have an unhealthy interest in all things thief-like – try safe-cracking, lock-picking, signature forgery, politics, etc. Above all try to make the fact you are now criminal (though petty) completely obvious and deny it all with a disarming smile: ('I thief, sir? Nooo couldn't have been me. No idea where your wallet is, sir.')

Paranoids   Practise studying every conversation for the slightest hint of mockery. Install bugs in the neighbour's house/apartment/hovel, etc. Write down every conversation, checking scrupulously for hints of bad feelings against you. Install a rear-view mirror on your baseball cap. Develop an interest in astronomy, and buy a huge pair of binoculars, telescope, to track the movements of the local people.

Hysterics   Have a good laugh – then possibly a good cry. Overact about any films you might watch, books you might read, news you might hear, jokes you might find vaguely funny, jokes you don't find vaguely funny, etc. Just be interested in manic sorts of things – like indoor sports (e.g. table tennis), and throw a tantrum if you lose.

Lunatics   Nurture quite normal interests, except for full moons, when you develop psychopathic interests (horror movies, horror novels, fantasy wargaming, etc.)

Step Three: Clothing

Clothing conveys a lot about the way you tackle the sport of being a teenager – a sort of team strip or number. Here are suggestions, but be creative.

Introverts Plain clothes are the answer here. Keep it sort of early fifties suburbia – subdued jumpers are one good thing to wear. Never ever wear T-shirts, shorts or other summer clothing.

Extroverts Wear anything you won't get arrested for but try to overdress in garish, clashing garments. If black is in, wear white, if red is in, wear green. No one will notice how badly dressed you are if you are confident enough.

Egocentrics Wear whatever you like, with badges saying things like 'Only visiting this planet' or 'Aliens visit Earth? You gotta be joking!' etc.

Morbid Wear long, black winter clothing, whether it is summer, winter, spring or autumn. If anyone asks you how you wear such bright colours, answer – 'I want to die.'

Hypochondriacs Wear sensible clothing for the winter, and constantly sunbathe in the summer. If anyone tells you that you can get skin-cancer that way, run down to the casualty department of the hospital immediately.

Then round the bend Wear fairly normal clothing except for hysterical individuals who should only be seen in a tear-stained nightshirt/dress. Paranoid people should, as mentioned before, have a baseball cap with a rear-view mirror fitted.

Last Word

Just remember being a Teenager is a dynamic process, occurring in phases. Don't be scared to suddenly swap from being an extrovert to being an introvert and then go hysterical. Also: remember that Teenagerism is just a pastime to puzzle/entertain/ignore your parents and your friends/acquaintances, otherwise you are free to be quite normal.

Daniel Sedgwick (11)   **Daniel Sedgwick (11)**

*The Arm

The arm was put there by Mum
Before she went
Or was it Dad before he left?
Or maybe it got there on its own two legs.
Or by the man who goes to every boy's house
And puts an arm by his bed.

I take a bite from the arm.
And there's a red spider inside it.
It pulls some of my teeth out.

After an hour I turn into a spider
Just like the one I'd eaten.

Rebecca Hardie (13)

The Stomach of Amelia Frissle

A short while ago, I used to suffer from cravings that were somewhat ... well, very ... or rather to the extremity of being ... unusual. It was a bit like being a chocaholic really, only I wasn't one, because I didn't have a passion for eating chocolate; I had a passion for eating soil. Only in small quantities, mind, and I always brushed my teeth afterwards.

As Mum soon discovered, there were advantages to having such a habit. We grew our own potatoes, so the soil always had to be removed from them.

'Amelia!' Mum would call. 'I've got nine spuds to be done, please. Hurry up!'

Most teenage girls wouldn't exactly jump for joy upon hearing that, but I assure you, I did. To me, it was a golden opportunity, not to be missed.

Now you think that I was a very peculiar person, but I assure you that I wasn't the only one in the world who did this. A few years previously, there had been a woman on the news who ate the soil off potatoes. That was what inspired the idea in the first place; so I sampled a little soil and drew the conclusion that it was ten times better than a Mars bar. So please do not think ill of me; it just goes to show that I'm a fascinating person, doesn't it – well, I think I'm a fascinating person.

Anyway, to continue with my story. I was at school one day, in the playground, reading the problem page of a magazine with my best friend, Corel Grayson.

'Hey, look at this one,' said Corel. ' "Dear Joan, I have this problem." Oh, what a surprise. "There's this boy at school I really like and I think he likes me. The thing is he's already got a girlfriend and ..." Amelia, what's up?'

'I . . . I feel strange,' I responded faintly.

Indeed, I had just experienced a peculiar and highly unpleasant sensation in my stomach. Sort of a tickling pain, but not something one can easily put into words. I had been having these sensations for a number of days now and they had been getting progressively more severe.

'In what way do you feel strange?' asked Corel.

'It's my stomach.'

'W-what about it?'

'Feels strange.'

'Yes, I know that.'

'Feels awful.'

'Do you want to go to the medical room?'

The following afternoon, I sat next to my mother in the waiting room, feeling ill and depressed. She had become very concerned for my health and had telephoned the doctor's to ask if I could have an appointment fitted in.

An excited toddler wobbled across the room, brandishing a picture book. Then the plastic toy box in the corner of the room caught his eye. He seemed to forget about the book and absently dropped it as he tottered over to the toy box. In this he began to rummage, until, with a squeal, he extracted . . . half (this is a rough estimation) a teddy bear.

'He's got no bottom,' the toddler stated to the sympathetic audience of his mother and an elderly gentleman, who seemed to be quite enamoured with him.

The head of Dr Mercel appeared at the door. 'Amelia Frissle,' she announced. I winced. For someone of my tender years (fourteen to be exact) to have one's surname announced to the public is quite an ordeal, when it happens to be Frissle.

It must have been a very wilting, depressed me that traipsed after my mother. We followed Dr Mercel into her surgery. I seated myself and waited for her to spin round in the swivel chair and face me.

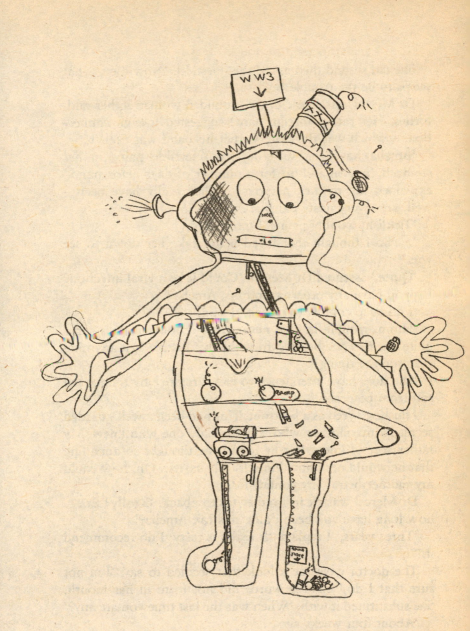

Oliver Densham (12)

She did so and then asked the question. 'Now then, what seems to be the trouble?'

Dr Mercel was a placid, well-rounded woman in her mid-forties. Her rather foreign name suggested foreign connections – which was the case, for her husband was French.

'Amelia has been suffering from terrible pains in her stomach, and on and off for a number of days beforehand,' explained my mother, nervously. 'They really have been – well, are – very nasty pains . . .'

'Ticklish, wobbly pains,' I interjected.

'. . . So I thought that I had better take her down to see you.'

'Quite,' assented Dr Mercel. 'Could it be a viral infection? Do you have any other symptoms, Amelia?'

'I do keep coming over sick,' I said.

'Hmm, trouble is, I've never really come across a virus quite like this one before,' frowned the doctor. 'Is it anything that you are doing?'

'She does have a tendency to er . . . remove by tongue the soil from potatoes.'

I flushed as red as a beetroot. This had been a well-guarded secret by my mother, who was the only one who knew. My father sort of knew, but he found the thought so appalling that he would not allow himself to believe it. Oh, how could my mother betray my confidence?

Dr Mercel was clearly rather taken aback. 'Really? Er . . . how long have you been doing this for, Amelia?'

'Three years,' I replied. 'It really is tasty: I do recommend it.'

The doctor gave me a look that seemed to say, 'I'm not sure that I do,' but the words did not form in her mouth. She substituted it with, 'When was the last time you ate any?'

'About four weeks ago . . .'

'Oh yes, I remember,' beamed my mother. 'I had quite a

few spuds to be done that day.' (I think that this was intended to serve as encouragement to me.)

'I don't eat it very often,' I finished.

'Hmmm,' frowned Dr Mercel. 'If you've been eating it for three years, I expect you have developed a resistance to any virus that you might catch from it. You say you've never had these pains before?'

'Never.'

'And they tickle and wobble?'

'Yes.'

'What an unpleasant nature they are of! It does sound as if possibly you have something trapped in your stomach. I think an X-ray would be in order.'

I suddenly reeled over as my pain grew ten times worse and fluttered about as if it were a butterfly.

'Is that the pain?' enquired Dr Mercel.

'Yes!' I choked.

It was not long before my mother and I found ourselves in the process of transportation to the hospital. The doctor had come to the decision that I had better have my X-ray at once; for being unsure of the reason for my discomfort, she could not offer something for it and be happy in the knowledge that I would find it agreeable.

The length of time for which my mother and myself sat in the waiting room is questionable. I spent a good proportion of the time asleep, wakening at intervals to find my mother killing the time with a copy of *Stories and Puzzles for Younger Children*; the only reading material available on the otherwise bare reading table. Twice Mum went to phone my dad and explain. Apparently Dad offered to come over and wait with us, but my mother thought that there was little point.

At last, my mother shook me awake and informed me that the radiographer was ready.

Oh! The days that followed I lived in agony! I did not attend school of course, and the days dragged on slowly. The pains were increasing a little and, as I came to realize, I made them worse every time I ate or drank. It did not take my mother long to come to a decision: I could not go on like this! I would have to return to hospital.

The hospital's solution was simple; they would numb my stomach and then keep me under observation. Mum, too, stuck to me like a magnet. Never have I in my life seen her pray so much! Only at the very best of times have I known her to remember 'Our Father' before she goes to sleep. At home we had all been praying that the results would soon be ready and that I could be treated. Now, in addition to this, my mother was constantly murmuring pleas that I should not react disagreeably to the painkiller.

It seemed that by my return to hospital, the results were speeded up. Dr Mercel sent them to the hospital.

I was reading a comic, when a hospital doctor, name of Partridge, approached my bed looking grave.

'I'd like to speak alone with your mum for a few minutes,' he said.

I was left alone, with wide open eyes and a pounding heart. If I had a nervous tummy ache, I couldn't feel it. I must have waited for about ten minutes, but it seemed more like a decade.

Finally, my mother and Dr Partridge came in sight. He still looked serious, but Mum's expression had transformed. Her face now wore an excited, surprised look. They came to a halt when they reached my bed.

'Amelia,' began the doctor. 'Now, what I have to tell you will make you very surprised, in fact, it'll give you a big shock.'

I braced myself for the worst.

'Perhaps I didn't say that very well,' he said hastily.

116

'I mean I want you to prepare yourself. Take your time now.'

'I just want to know,' I said faintly.

'Take your time,' repeated Dr Partridge, patiently, 'please.'

I tried, really I did, but I just couldn't do it. 'I can't wait!' I burst out with renewed energy. 'I've got to know! Please, please tell me!'

He took a deep breath. 'All right, all right. I'll come straight to the point. You have a small tree developing in your stomach.'

My newly found energy rapidly dissolved. 'A tree?' I echoed weakly. 'You're joking.'

'I wish I was.'

'It does sound a bit . . . far fetched.'

'The X-ray clearly showed a sapling in your tummy. Your Mum told me that you have a habit of eating soil.'

I reddened.

'No need for embarrassment . . . we all have our little habits – heh, heh.'

'Ho ho.'

'E-hem. Well, er, to continue. It seems that you must have swallowed a pip from a piece of fruit which has miraculously implanted itself in your intestines.'

I could use half of a dictionary to describe my immediate emotions. However, one can easily imagine how I felt. How would you, had Dr Partridge just informed you you had a tree in your stomach?

I lay on my bed. Something amazing had just happened. It wasn't the tree – I had already had the natural thoughts: how had this happened, how had it grown without light, did light enter my body when I opened my mouth, how would the tree be removed, would it be painful, would I be famous . . . the list is endless.

One of my questions was soon to be answered. The tree would be chemically dissolved said Dr Partridge. However, that had been during the previous day, the day on which I acquired the knowledge that my intestines yielded a tree.

Five minutes earlier, my mother had been sitting at the foot of my bed, explaining.

'There's an American scientist over in this part of England,' she had said. 'He has heard about your sapling – news travels fast you know – and he has asked Dr Partridge and myself if it would be possible for you to have it surgically removed.'

'No way!'

'It would be a far more complicated procedure,' she admitted. 'However, it would mean that he could perform many experiments that could not otherwise be done. The results might be exciting.'

'I'm not doing it!'

'He has offered us a . . . substantial amount of money if we comply.'

She whispered something in my ear that made my eyes open wide.

'Now don't you repeat that to anyone,' she continued. 'I don't want it broadcast.'

'I won't. Would I get anything out of it?'

'Yes, your father and I have discussed it.'

She whispered another 'substantial' sum. I fairly leapt out of my bed. This shed a whole new light on things.

'I'll do it, I'll do it!' I cried.

'Amelia, I don't want you jumping in with both feet. Give it some careful thought first. I don't want you regretting your decision.'

What she said was to little effect however, for I had already made up my mind.

My hand is tiring of the writing, so only briefly shall I describe the events that transpired during the late morning and afternoon.

My mother came to make certain that I was 'absolutely sure' of my decision. Of course I was, I replied; after all,

118

I was doing them a big favour. Besides, I might be the source of a great scientific break-through.

'In what?' queried my father sarcastically.

'In . . . biology,' I mumbled, surprised.

This was succeeded by an interview with the American scientist. To protect his identity, I shall call him Mr Laugh-a-lot, because he laughs every time he speaks.

After this, I had a visit from Corel Grayson, who presented me with the alarming news that the school knew of my partiality to soil and of the sapling in my stomach.

'Don't work yourself up,' she said soothingly. 'Nobody minds. They treat you as some kind of heroine. Some are jealous.'

My eyes flicked open. They blinked. I yawned. I looked at the clock opposite my bed. The time was twenty-three minutes to twelve. Then I realized. I had had the operation. Furthermore, I was on a drip! I remembered that Mr Laugh-a-lot had said I would be unable to eat in the form of solids for some while.

A nurse was bent over me. 'Hello, Amelia,' she beamed. 'How do you feel?'

'Drowsy,' I yawned.

'Have you seen it?'

'What, the drip?'

'No. Look to your right.'

There I saw it, on my bedside cabinet. A tinted glass dome. The nurse raised the dome to reveal a plant pot containing a tiny tree, no more than six centimetres in height.

'It's already been discovered that the tree can only take a certain amount of light,' she explained. 'It's an orange tree,' she added, as if I had just given birth to a baby and she was naming its sex. Indeed, I felt as if that was what was happening.

My recovery was rapid. There were many experiments to

be carried out and many exciting discoveries made. Mr Laugh-a-lot is currently writing a book about it. I expect I'll be in all the new encyclopedias too.

The orange tree (named Ho-ho) grows rapidly in a shaded corner of our garden. It is somewhat smaller than most orange trees of its age, but there is otherwise no difference.

So there you have it. I achieved fame and, in a way, fortune. Furthermore, I am a changed person. For one thing, I no longer eat soil. The mere trouble of a slight stomach ache serves me as a warning against it.

Miss Bricket, English teacher of schoolgirl Amelia Frissle, ticked the essay. 'Shows you do have a brain,' she commented underneath. It had been a surprise to Miss Bricket, whose experience had been that Amelia did not know where her sentences began or ended.

'Needs editing, of course,' she thought. 'But at least she has made an effort. The ending is true; she has changed.'

William Paul (7)

My Yummy Friends

It was pocket-money day and William asked his mum if he could go to the sweetie shop.

I would like to buy a lollipop, he said.

All right, his mum said. Here is the money. Get me a loaf of bread too. Off you go.

William took the one pound note and walked off down the street. He went in to the shop on the corner and bought a strawberry lollipop. When he came out of the shop it melted and fell on the ground at his feet.

At the next shop he bought a loaf of bread to take home to make into toast. When he put the first slice of bread in to the toaster after a few minutes out popped a bread man with arms and legs.

I will call you Jimmy, said William. I hope we can be friends.

Yes, said bread man Jimmy.

Jimmy quickly grew to be the same size as William. But once honey was spread over his tummy William could not resist a bite.

First William ate one arm then the other arm then a leg then the other leg. Suddenly there was none of Jimmy left to eat but his head.

Cheerio, said William. It has been nice knowing you.

He put another slice into the toaster. The next bread man popped up.

Hello there, he said.

Honey or jam, asked William. You and I must get to know each other better.

Katherine Walker (7)

Bad Habits

My bad habit is sucking my thumb. When people see me doing it they say don't do that it's babyish. People don't like it because I have a rather noisy thumb. My daddy's bad habit is spitting into the sink. When Mummy sees or hears him she is very cross. Michael's bad habit is reading when the lights are turned out. I do it too.

Yolanda Barton (8)

The Elephant in my Kitchen

'Guess what, guys?
There is . . .
An ELEPHANT in my kitchen!'
'No!'
'Yes! It eats things we put
In the washing basket.
It's white, and I saw it today!'
And slowly but surely the message goes round
from Woodcraft Club, to the school playground.
The children gather at lunch-tables and mutter,
Instead of eating their bread-and-butter.
Straight after school, rush-hour begins,
For children,
As the school bell rings.

Yolanda Barton (8)

And everyone knows, teachers, friend,
Football supporters at the 'World's End',
Of the WHITE ELEPHANT.
And over the wall they jump in scores,
And over patios and floors,
To where SOMETHING droops out of the window.
Everybody's in a funk,
That certainly *isn't* an elephant's trunk.
They don't know that, inside,
I, and the tumble dryer elephant hide.

Dinna Plunk the Jorry Bool!

Morag:	Dinna do that, birl the jorry bool . . . not plunk it.
Duncan:	I'm awae sorry, Morag, but by jings isna it stupid.
Morag:	It's me jorry bool, I'll do wi it as I please.
Duncan:	Aye, Aye, but ye'll ruin it that way.
Morag:	Yer just try'n to git your own way, ye chanty rassler.
Duncan:	Och! Yer jus be'n selfish, Morag, hang on here a wee minute, there's a stoater of a lassy over there.
Morag:	I thought I was your bonny girlfriend.
Duncan:	Throw yersel in the stank, Morag . . . Yer the chanty rassler now aren't ya, ha! ha! ha!
Morag:	Am not a chanty rassler . . . I know yer just feart of me an' I'll tell the whole world.
Duncan:	You would na dare.

Morag:	I would and they'd think you were yorlin.
Duncan:	They'd think I was gallus for dumpin ye.
Morag:	Not on yer Nelly! I dumped you.
Duncan:	Well am having the bonny lassy wi good legs . . . insted.
Morag:	By jings the cheek o' you . . . go play with yer dumb blonde, I'll not do yer homework for be'n the best chanty rassler ever.
Duncan:	And yer say I hae cheek . . . Ye don't know how wrong y'are.
Morag:	I'm leaving right now wi me jorry bool . . . and there hunk over ther will birl it wi me.
Duncan:	What hunk?!! Ohh, the spotty wee geek . . . some hunk.
Morag:	OK, no hunk . . . but ye are ment ta be ma boyfriend . . . at least ma friend.
Duncan:	Right, Morag, we'll be friends . . . and I'll birl yer jorry bool.

Mark Warren (5)

*be be be quiet

be be be quiet
in assembly
be be be loud in
the playground
be be be good in school
be be be bad in your
dreams

WORRYING THE CLOUDS

Victoria Moss (12)

Martin Beek (8)

Watching

Watching the trees lose their leaves.
Watching leaves change colour
in the Autumn.
And getting green in the spring
It's quite boring for me
Watching plants . . .
Getting older every year.

Lauren Coffey (9)

*Autumn

It begins with street lamps showing
their bright faces as we show our cold.
The way we pull on wellies over two pairs
of woolly socks, the struggle of the thick jumper,
'Mum, do I have to wear this one?' The air
hardens your bones like a rusty robot.
The rustle of leaves as people walk to find
wood for a glowing fire; as they fall
like grabbing hands, they try to decorate
the hall, no need for paint, no need at all.
They rest the night under cars. The oak says,
'Go children, go and spread yourselves below.'

Julie Begum (8)

The smoke of Sunday night appears, a swirling
staircase into the sky that reddens like blood.
When the leaves fall they die; they dig
their tombs, and the sun, slowly, sadly,
lowers itself into the arms of the world.

Lucy Smith (10)

*Rain

My window is cold as I watch
Rain hammer the cars,
The long faces under coats,
And tall boots splash puddles.

Smudge creeps into the shed
With his soaking tail.
The roof plays music;
Falling elderberries join in,

With the creaky door, and the wind,
The garden is an orchestra.
The puddles greet raindrops
With jumps of joy. Below

There are storytellers: Look down,
Through and listen. As the sun shows
They fade away, and books, torn,
Falling apart, rustle down gutters.

Now, it's lunchtime for snails.
They're everywhere! Smudge reappears,
Smiles come back to life,
And lights are turned off.

Wind Ways

I am the wind.
It is a party for me.
I can hurl through the door
without any key.
I can blow the chair out the window.
I can shake the tree.
I can jump on the washing line
to make it fall down.
I am the draught that comes into
your bedroom at night.
I can strip the wallpaper off
your bedroom wall.
I can suck your curtains out the window.
I can tear up your best plant.
I can lift the slates off the roof.
I will lift your house up.
Then after that rage
I will go to sleep.

Two Days of Snow

A shadow stalks over the land.
Calm sea,
Turns to rolling swells,
As the cloud draws nearer.
It rears above,
Billow upon billow
And suddenly unfolds.

Feathers float in a frenzy
Falling,
Falling,
To smother the earth.

And soon it is quiet,
The blanket has settled,
Silently
A white world laid to rest

But still snow is falling,
Layer upon layer,
Deeper and deeper,
All
Sleeps and waits.
Nothing moves,
Till first light.

The children wake first,
To a mittened morning.
Sledges are dragged out,
Ice skates fitted.
As the first snowmen are completed,

The adults wake,
And look out on a busy landscape.
Then a slight pattering,
As white flakes fall,
On abandoned fair-weather pastimes;
The swings, the bikes, the balls.

And soon the wind grows,
Turning waves to great white horses.
Soft snow to stinging hailstones,
And raw-faced children run for shelter.

But soon the blizzard dies.
Red noses,
Puffed cheeks emerge,

The icy road lies,
Smothered,
Beneath the glittered sky.
As sledges speed,
Or carve their courses,
Down whitewashed fields,
More snow drifts,
Down,
Down;
As snowmen's uncompleted bodies,
Are rolled round gardens;
Still it falls.

Evening closes in,
Activity draws, reluctantly, to an end,
Children relax by warm fires,
Waiting, for a new day
To shine its light
On freshly fallen snow.
When fun will fly through the air with snowballs,
Gloved hands grip tight
As faded sleighs
Charge down slopes.

But when today draws into tomorrow,
A slight dripping can be heard,
Over the white expanse of snow.

All
Wakes to a dappled land.
Patches of snow,
As faded as the sleighs
Which now sit,
And wait,
For more winter days.

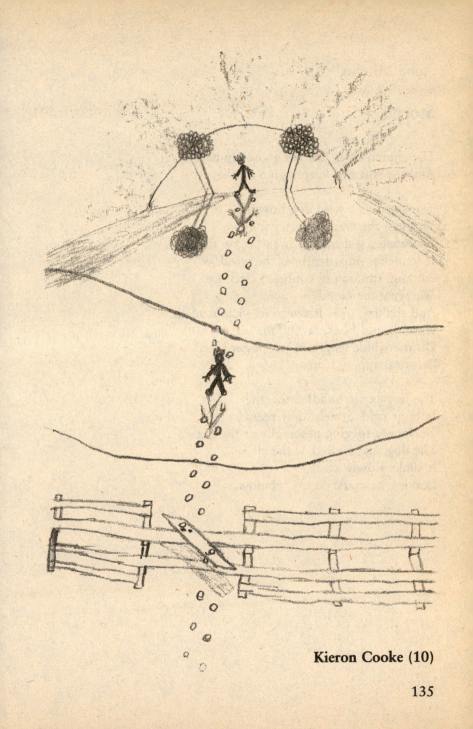

Kieron Cooke (10)

Anna Mitchell (8)

Storm

The church clock chimes a ghostly twelve
And the storm is keeping me awake.

The storm is a wild dog howling
Through the crack in my window
The wind's wet muzzle breathes on the glass
It scratches impatiently at the window
Panting, running in confused circles,
Worrying the clouds
And shaking trees between its vicious teeth.
It snarls and bites, tasting the air
On the whole length of its tongue
Before snapping it up.

The horses are huddled together
In their field. Stately, they rear,
No longer tugging peacefully at the grass.
The dog snaps, tired of the chase.
It slinks slowly away,
Leaving its mark on my window.

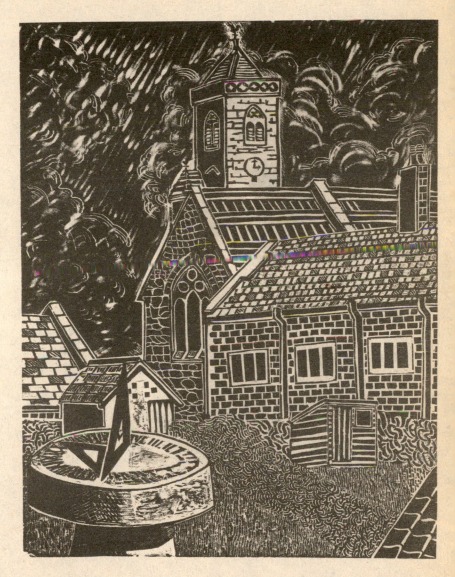

Robert Pepper (15)

Laura Cliff (11)

Tim Thwaites (11)

*The Snowslide's Reply

Tiny man,
In your little house of ice,
I have listened to your prayer,
And I do not agree with you.

Desperate man,
It is my reputation to be cruel,
I shall not let you off.
Your prayer was a waste of time.

Silly man,
I'll never stop my avalanche.
I do not care about your wife and children,
Or your little house.

Dying man,
Curse your lucky stars.
I'm going to start the snow going.
Say goodbye, little man.

Geoffrey Hopper (8)

Who Came?

footprints in the snow
who was it came in
the night taking the
short cut?

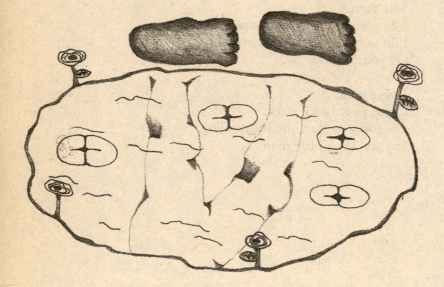

Alec Storey (10)

x

140

THROUGH CROOKS AND CRANNIES

Charles Knott (12) and James Emsell (12)

Marilyn Rust (14)

Birth of a Calf

When I first saw him
His hooves were sticking out of his mother,
Pink and new!

His mother ambled across the field . . .
A stream of heifers following.
She rolled over in the loose straw
That littered the ground by the feed cage.

The cows chased away the heifers
And gathered around her . . .
Like midwives, mooing encouragement,
Lathering her face
With thick spongy tongues.

She grunted as she pushed,
Letting out new life.
Then, with one last heave of pain,
He slithered out,
Followed by a red ribbon
Of after birth,
Striped with blue.

And there he lay,
A damp heap of rusty brown
Plastered with straw,
His hair stuck out at all angles,
As though brushed backwards.

Marilyn Rust (14)

She nudged him to his hooves.
He tried to stand
On unsure stick legs.
He wobbled and fell.
Again he tried, never giving up . . .

Until at last he stood,
Tried to reach his mother's udders.
But she pushed him away . . .
She had to see him; he needed to be washed.
Every time she pushed him away,

Until she was sure he was clean.
Only then could he feed;
That scruffy little urchin
Was now a beauty in his own right.

And there they stood
Mother and son
Ready for the *WORLD*!

Daniel Sedgwick (11)

*Cat

I am the lolling, curled up in the chair,
in the airing cupboard,
in trees,
on roofs, in drawers,
behind closed curtains.

I am the dragging of dead thrushes
across the garden,
I am the raider of nests,
the fighter.
I am the flurry of teeth and claws,
the grabber of fingers.

I am the creeping down low,
the dead straight look,
zip,
the pounce.

I am the purr on someone's lap,
the big wall in the fight.

I am the king of wailing that makes
people throw boots at me.
I am the green headlights
piercing the dark.

I am the stalking along the path,
the pushing of doors open
with my nose,

the doing of those things you don't want me to do,
the not doing of those things you want me to do.

Bethany Beddoes (8)

The Hookoo Birds

Chapter 1:   Emily disappears

One cold, rainy morning Kate looked through her window. She was cross and angry at the thought of her rounders' game being cancelled. Kate suddenly picked up her ragdoll called Emily, and threw her out of the window. As she watched Emily fall to the ground some mysterious shadows appeared, Kate could see Emily no more. Then Kate's mother came upstairs and poked her head round the door. Kate turned and asked what she wanted.

'I just wondered,' said her mother, 'if you want to help me sort out the cupboard downstairs.'

'No, thanks,' said Kate miserably. As she turned back to the window the shadows had gone and so had Emily!

Chapter 2:   The phone call

A few moments later the phone rang.

'I'll get it,' called Kate loudly. But when she had got downstairs her biggest sister Fran had got there before her.

'Right, yes, I'll tell her, thank you, bye,' Kate heard her say.

'Who was that?' Kate demanded.

'Oh, nobody you will know about until you say I look really pretty.'

Kate was almost sick when she had said it. Fran was dressed in a blue top with black and white spots which looked like bird droppings, her trousers were black with brown squares which Kate thought looked like a cat with muddy paws had run over her. Kate thought she looked awful. 'Well, what did that person on the phone say then?' asked Kate.

'Oh, just to tell you your rounders game will be cancelled,' smirked Fran.

Chapter 3:   What were those shadows?

Kate decided she had to do something to keep herself occupied. As she walked into the dining room she saw her mother clearing out the cupboard.

'Would you like to help me?' she asked, for what seemed like the tenth time to poor Kate.

'OK,' she mumbled under her breath. As she helped her mother clear out the cupboard she saw something which caught her eye, it was a picture of herself with no clothes on. She snatched it up quickly when her mother turned her head, for if Fran got hold of it there would be trouble. Just then outside she saw some black shadows. Kate remembered what she had seen out of the window and decided to investigate. As Kate got nearer she heard a rustling behind the garden shed, she peeped round but there was nothing there. Kate went through the back door into the lounge, but soon got shooed out for making muddy footprints on their new carpet they got from Cuddly Carpets in the sale. As Kate's lounge is pink and grey they had a lot of arguments over the colour. Kate's mother wanted pink with light grey dashes and her father wanted grey and pink marbled together. In the end Kate's father won and for a week her mother was sulky. Anyway, just then Edward walked in that's Kate's brother.

'What have you done?' said Kate at the haircut.

Chapter 4: Kate's father and the haircut

Kate's brother Edward sat down frowning at Kate after her remark. He then met Fran. Now when you've done something wrong you don't want to bump into Fran, for one thing she goes and tells Kate's mum or dad, possibly her dad for he has a dreadful temper at times, and for another she starts giggling and spluttering. Kate's dad was a social worker which meant he worked all day long and as I have mentioned before he has an awful temper, and usually wears smart trousers and a polo neck. Kate's mother was kind but firm, she always wears pretty frocks and her hair is long which is always tied up in a bun. Fran ran off to tell her father about Edward's haircut giggling as she went, now if there's one thing Kate's father can't stand it's giggly girls. So as soon as Fran entered her father's bedroom she put on a sweet smile. At this time Kate's father was very busy sorting out his ties. He was a tiny bit cross at being disturbed but he saw Fran's sweet smile and returned it joyfully. 'Hello, my little cherry pie,' he said gently. Fran very suddenly blurted out about

Edward's haircut. Kate's father nearly exploded. When he saw Edward he did explode.

Chapter 5: The explosion

As Kate was watching *Noddy*, at the same time she was trying to listen to what was going on in the hallway.

'By the way,' said her father, 'how many times have you had mistakes like this and after I have told you never to do it again.'

He was now shouting. I was hoping our neighbours were enjoying the row. Kate's family shouted at Edward for the next ten minutes. Then Kate's father picked up his coat and Edward's hat. Kate caught a glimpse out of the door – his hair was green with red streaks and very noticeable.

A few hours later Kate was chomping away on an iced-bun when the phone rang. Fran answered, as usual. It was her father saying he was at the barbers. Kate suddenly saw some big birds black as night with beaks one metre long. Kate put on her now very muddy boots and went outside dropping her half eaten bun on the carpet as she went. Laying on a table lay Emily, every bird was dancing around her.

'What are you doing?' Kate asked astonished.

All the birds turned. Kate had to dodge to prevent getting knocked over with their beaks.

'We are praising our prized possession,' said the largest bird.

'Why is my ragdoll your prized possession?' Kate replied.

'We are Hookoo birds,' they said.

Chapter 6: Hookoo birds come to stay

That night Kate asked her mother if she could have a pet. 'Certainly,' said her mother pleased at the idea. 'What sort of pet?'

'Birds,' said Kate definitely. 'Shall I get them?' added Kate.

'Where from?' she asked curious and startled.

'From behind the shed there are *HOOKOO BIRDS*.'

Kate's mother gasped. 'Show me,' she demanded.

As Kate led her behind the shed Kate's mother saw them. At once she fell in love with them.

'Of course you can keep them,' said her mother. Not really considering her husband's ideas at all.

'Where shall I keep them?' asked Kate getting excited.

Her mother considered this, then she bluntly said, 'In the garage tonight.'

When everybody was sat down eating chicken casserole silently, Kate broke the silence. 'Mother bought me some birds today,' she said. 'She what!' cried her father. 'Where?'

'That's right,' said Kate's mother calmly, 'Hookoo birds.'

'Well, what are they meant to be for goodness sake?'

'They are big birds staying in the garage tonight,' said her mother.

'Smashing,' said Edward.

'Wizard!' cried Fran.

'Well, it looks like it's four against one,' said Kate's mother smiling.

'Oh, all right, you can keep the silly fat feathered birds,' said Kate's father. 'But they cannot stay in my garage to-morrow night.'

Next morning at breakfast Kate's father brought up the subject about his garage.

'Yes, I'm calling in the builders,' said his wife.

'Brilliant,' shouted Kate her mouth full of burnt toast as the toaster had broken.

'Don't talk with your mouth full,' said her mother sounding cross, as she was very strict about meal manners.

The builders arrived at exactly ten and started to build the garage. When they had finished the Hookoo birds moved in. Kate's father was slightly annoyed at the expense but he soon got over it. The Hookoo birds found it a very nice home and seemed pleased. Every morning Kate fed the Hookoo birds on leftovers from her meals, if there was any that is. But the Hookoo birds never seemed to mind what they ate as long as they ate something. And even Kate's father has learnt to adore the Hookoo birds.

Cressida Wilcox (15)

*Crow

A sticky black lump of crow
Fell down into the fireplace.
While my back was turned
He hop-hopped
Under my chair.

I turned and saw him
Choke, gasp in my throat.
Then I calmed, I observed him
Exposed.
Little satan
Fallen from his rotting nest
At the top of my chimney.

I scooped him up,
Bird of air
Thick black tar clot
Of this ice sky.
At first no resistance,
But his little fear brewed within,
His shiny claws dug red into white skin.
His grotty little heart hammered.

I felt his wings
Try to unfold in my grasp.
I felt the tiny ache of his effort,
His ache for freedom
Young crow.

He uttered a soundless cry
Head on one side,
Beady-eyed crow.
Disgust at the white rashy skin
Flaking round his beak,
His hands were caked and crusted
Dirty man.

His tiny chest heaved as he fought:

Suddenly

I have a bird in my hands!

I released him out of my window
Sticky black lump.

Down,
Down he plummeted.

My mind

Split-second reasoning:
Not time to catch him
Never run down in time
Let him fall
your conscience!
Down he tumbled.
I turned away and started to try and forget him

But triumphant squawk in air.
I didn't have to turn back
To see his success.
Yet I did, and was witness to his foul glory
Over air.
Pride is me.
I will feel pleased for a long time.

Calum Brown (10)

Trapped Bird

Helplessly flapping
Wings beating against cold stone
Everything strange –
To him we are foe

He lands on a post
Chest beating in and out
Then he bolts –
A final try.

He flies through the door
To freedom –
But falls and lies in the ferns

Gently, I pick him up
My fingers slide along the feathered back
For a second frightened eyes
Look into mine –

And he flies away!

Bethan Whitham (13)

Geraldine Clarke (13)

154

Douglas Swinyard (11)

The Bat

The bat, like a bell,
Hangs upside down;
Feet, like tiny grappling hooks,
Cling to the branch.
His rusty fur
And cat-like ears
Blend with the bark.
People say he is blind
But he sees with sound,
Sending out
High bell tones
That only he can hear.

Zara Jackman (13)

155

Paul Trudgill (13)

*The Spider

The spider,
an eight-legged rope shop,
anywhere and everywhere.
It crawls constantly through crooks and crannies,
webbing its way from wall to wall,
abseiling across acres of architecture.
It sneaks silently from room to room,
like a burglar in a black suit,
day or night unnoticed.
Then it darts across the piled carpet,
like a runner on rough terrain.
Daringly, it watches you,
like a peeping Tom,
eight retracting legs,
curling up in to a Velcro ball,
to hide.

Russell Welham (10)

Spider

I saw the blob of black paint
lying on the floor,
the very small top hat,
and the eye pupil hanging
on a string.
It was the spider.

Neil Kent (12)

156

Lucy Smith (10)

Louise Bevan (9)

*Hawk

Waits
above the cornfield
his claws
sunk in the clouds
sharp
knives in the feathers
he turns
the world around
and stops
the hearts of rabbits.

Thomas Smith (5)

Lazy Lizard

I'm a lazy lizard
And I sit on a rock
The sun shines on my back
I'm getting very hot
I open one big green eye
And look around for flies
I catch them with my sticky tongue
The sun is hot and dries my scaly skin
Until it's hard and bumpy.
My only friend in the desert
Is a snake and he is grumpy.
So I sit on my rock
The sun is hot on my back
I look bumpy and ugly
But I am a nice chap.

Kelly Mills (12)

Paul Trudgill (13)

*The Otter

The otter, a small shiny land cruiser,
whips along close to the ground,
then slips in to the water,
to act just like an amphibious tank.
But it can be motionless,
loitering like a woman in a salon,
its fur flat and finely combed,
then coated thickly with gel.
Its eyes are tiny silver shiny balls,
bouncing from side to side.
Claws grip like a tractor's anti-skid system
clawing its way up a mud bank.
The tongue laps at unbeatable speed, milk
from the wreckage of a broken milk bottle.
Then, lady-like, he walks back to his holt.

Gavin Thurlow (14)

*Whale . . .

Martin MacDonald (13)

I uncurl the sea,
And you're there.
Staring with oyster eyes
Set in deep curves of muscle.
Your streamlined back,
Like black silk over hot wax.
Barnacles cling to your chin
Like limpet mines to an old ship.
Your giant mouth opens,
Releasing an eerie wailing cry . . .
Your air vent,
Shaped like a milk bottle nozzle,
Opens and lets out hot air,
Creating a spout of steam . . .
Surely you must be admired
For your knowledge.
But you are more known for meat, or fat . . .
You bear a deep scar to prove it,
A deep gash in your side,
Cut like a slice of watermelon.
The spear fell out long ago.
And now you are dying.
The last whale
Floats to the surface,
Like a giant island . . .

Sally Gillo (8)

The Whale

Martin MacDonald (13)

I've never seen a whale,
Because I don't go out to sea.
So why do I care about them?
One day I will go
And stand there at the side of a ship
And wait.
But will they still be there?
Would it be a waste of time,
Or would it be worth it?
I would love to see a trembling in the water.
I would love to feel the cold water spray me
Out of its spout.
To think about cool water gives me the shivers.
It makes my body feel the whale's.
It makes me feel as if I've just
Got out of bed and got back in again:
It makes my teeth chatter with warmth.
When the sun sparkles on the whale's skin
It glimmers like a wet roof top.
When it is back in the water
It's back in its gloomy world.
It twirls and glides its tail.
It looks like the Great Wall of China.
It breaks the water to pieces
To be free again.

Nisha Doshi (6)

*The Hermit Crab's Morning

The hermit crab steps sideways,
Swiftly on the seabed.
Sulking sadly because he has no private shell.
Cold, shivering, terrified.
He wasn't born with one,
He needs to borrow one.
A Borrower!
He borrows shells to protect himself.
He doesn't want to be starters for lunch!

His long, thin feelers wave silently,
Searching for a shell.
He finds one,
Shaped like a trombone,
With a pointed cone.
Rough and tough,
Bumpy and lumpy.
Sandy brown, snowy crown!
It makes a comfy home.

Safe and protected,
The hermit crab steps sideways,
Swiftly on the seabed.
Happily hurrying, searching for food.
His eyes like baby olives on tiny stalks!
He spies his prey.
He grabs it, rips it,
Quickly shoves it in his mouth.
He has his starters for lunch!

Nisha Doshi (6)

THE HORIZON TAKES ME FURTHER

Joel Du Bois (12)

Craig Worlledge (11)

*to

to hear the earthworm
under the ground
to touch the noise
between my cat's whiskers
to hear myself thinking
trying to be right
to taste my reflection
in the mirror
to touch the squeak
of the prisoner's bed
as he gets up
for his execution
to paint the pike
hiding in the reeds
to paint my worries
and dangers all at the
bottom of my head
waiting to jump up.

Ysanne Friend (8)

Baby

A baby is a new-born child
That giggles, squeals and cries.
Cries that voices carry over mountains
And over hills.
Tears drip down its cheeks and create a lake.
Mummy comes to the rescue,
And wades up to her knees in her baby's tears.
But the baby is safe.
It is bobbing up and down in the water.

Lucy Burnett (8)

*Night

The stars blink at us like the
eyes of dead men from years ago,
caught in a tree.
I hear the kettle click like a
finger touching me on the heart,
and the earthquake of my dad's tummy.
We've trapped the night in the cellar;
it's so big we can't get it out.

Jenny Kitchener (8)

*Night

Night is a duvet settled down,
the giant black cat's tummy.
Stars are ancient scrolls
telling stories, the moon
is a ball between two stars of children;
it watches, trying to keep
its eyes open, so it can
be night and not day.
From my room, I hear
the spit of puddles
as the tyres fray them.

Clare Ripley (6)

Clair Honeywood (13)

Bindweed

The bindweed rises from the nettles,
Climbing up the posts in a spiral.
Its twisted arms stretch up the fence,
It blooms pendants along the thread,
Making the old post
Into a maypole of flowers.
And a wire fence
Is solid again with wilted hearts
As it weeps for a loved one
In bursts of white handkerchiefs.
It follows the tracks of the wire.
In the damp morning,
The bindweed clasps shut,
opening into a wind swept umbrella,
catching the light,
following its path.
Taking in its energy until
its rope stem clasps the flower
like a ring its gem.
And its leaves are ragged cat's ears.
The bindweed grows through the bush
like blood through the veins,
Layering the outside
In a progressive jig-saw.

Marcus Stockwell (10)

Victoria Fallon (7)

Mobile

It hangs in the air
like a bird.
It twists and turns
like a storm.
Where am I?
   Where was I?
It crashes and clashes
And suddenly dies down.
Like a storm dying down
on a sea of things.
Like dead people.
I don't know where
or what I am!

Jack Camplin (13)

*Drawing Pin

Staring out at me,
is myself,
miniaturized in gold plate,
rounded in a single centimetre circle.
The world is tiny,
the room around me is shrunken . . .
a huge oak table is just a drip of its former self.

172

Harry Brooks (12)

My face,
distorted,
round, wide-eyed, wondering,
my cheeks expand as I move nearer,
billowing like bloomers on a washing line.
My hand is elastic,
stretching,
bending.
My fingers reach out.
As they touch, they unite,
in one round balloon.
Just about to pop.
Then,
As I move my hand away,
it springs a leak and deflates,
just like my tyre as I pull the drawing pin out
of the black rubber.

Iain Mobbs (8)

*The Horizon

As I look northwards
Over the playing fields, over the river,
The horizon suddenly confines me to my quarters.
I can see no further.

In summer the yacht sails glide
Over the reservoir, tiny white flags:
In the distance the mallards fly.
I can see no further.

Hampton church can just be seen dimly
Gleaming, pale grey, sharp-edged against the blur,
Where the edge of London grows grimly.
I can see no further.

But if I go up the hill,
The horizon takes me further –
Over the green land where the
    sprawling city seems lying
Still – I can see further.

Robert Pleasance (12)

Jack Northover (10)

David Wall (12)

The Moors

Purple lavender,
Turned lighter by the setting sun,
Performs a Mexican wave
As the breeze sweeps my shoelaces in mad circles.

In the valley below
A path winds erratically towards the town,
An army of houses
Carrying their torches through the hills.

A solitary white house stands guard on the moors,
Like a spot on a black domino.
Shadows grasp for each other as the sun goes down,
The sky's fireball casting its last flames before my eyes.

LIKE THE FLICKERING OF
BLACK AND WHITE MOVIES

Peter Mansell-Jones (12)

Calum Brown (10)

Family Bible

Turn the yellowing pages,
Dust drifts,
On the tea-stained table.
My lost family of long ago,
Stare through the smudged memories,
Out,
On today's world.

Beginnings and ends,
Seen again by yet another generation,
Who wonder at the neat copperplate,
As it gives way to biro.

Long forgotten family moments,
White-woolled christenings,
Glass-clinking weddings,
Black-suited funerals,
How many before me,
Have touched this frail paper,
And wondered what names would mark,
The empty pages?
And who will look back at my name,
And wonder?

Kelly Buxton (12)

Roxanne Bailey (12)

Summer

The back garden.
No rest for a mum
Hanging out the washing.
No sky,
Only her blue eyes.

Porsche and Rocky
Pant in the shade,
Rizzo nests
In the cooking apple tree.
No movement

Lorries crawl,
Fridges tease,
Humming planes pass.
She pushes the pole up
And takes the basket indoors.

Nadja Coyne (16)

*A Picture of my Mother

Looking through a photo album,
I found a picture of my mother.
She was dressed in black,
And her long legs were crossed arrogantly.

She appeared again, this time in sequence.
Four pairs of eyes glinted in the white light,
Four perfect pouts were thrust toward the reflection,
Four carefully tousled fringes fell around a pale face.

The last picture was the largest,
The grainy reproduction of life,
Showed each slight line, each ginger freckle.
Her eyes stared across the camera and away from me.

I have looked for this girl, a thousand times,
I have longed for her quick, sweet smile.
I have watched for her green eyes and swinging walk,
Have waited to catch her on every street.
Will I know her when she finds me?

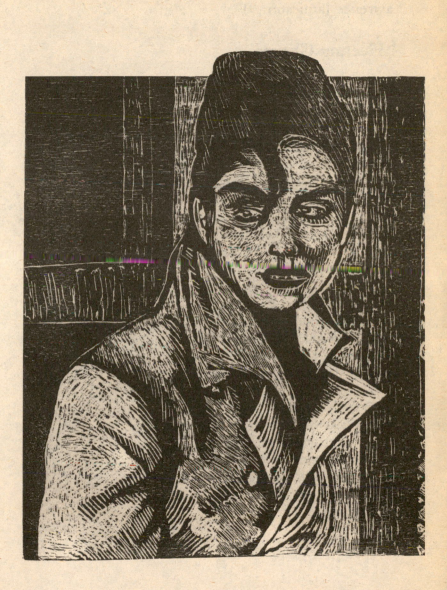

David Clark (15)

Lawrence Jamieson (9)

A Fleeting Glimpse

My dad wears glasses
and has curly hair – just like me.

Although he's twice as tall
Sometimes he rolls around on the floor
like a puppy dog – just like me.

In the garden we put up goals.
The flowers and bushes cheer as
Scotland takes on the world and he scores
a hat-trick – just like me.

Even when we must do serious things
like washing dishes, cleaning rooms
I can spot out the corner of my eye
that his mind is in other places
dreaming dreams – just like me.

Occasionally I glimpse passing time
like the flickering of black and white movies
my dad sometimes watches.
For a fleeting moment I recognize
that life continues on and
we really are our parents' children.

Jason Hunter (10)

Nicholas Tilson (10)

Aleck Green (8)

*The Fence

When my dad mends the fence
his hands go crazy,
they get blisters.
He kneels low,
concentrating – I know this
because his face is red.
His saw cuts the wood,
I can smell dirt on his shorts.

I'm standing by the window
watching him come back,
he says, 'Good, isn't it?'

Claire Smyth (6)

*Untitled

A cat comes to my garden and I stroke her fur. Her fur is
like a furry quilt. She comes to my garden very often. She
jumped up a tree and we could not get her down. We had to
get a ladder. We called Daddy. He found his word box at the
top of the tree. When he was five years old he lost his box.
Now he is five times ten years and he has found them. When
he came down the ladder I examined him in his words
but he **still** didn't know them. I told granny.

Nicholas Shopland (13)

'Rob'

My father told me a story.

It surprised me when he mentioned it. The use of the word 'telepathy' was intriguing, largely, I suppose, because I'd always seen him as a die-hard cynic.

The farm had taught him cynicism. Anyone who started romanticizing about 'the country life' would quickly aggravate him, though he would always keep quiet and laugh dryly to himself. The farm had taught him about the ceaseless battering of 'the elements', and the sadistic pleasure they derived from meaninglessly torturing those foolish enough to battle with them. Every slap in the face made him more bitter. Life wasn't easy – working from seven till late in the evening every day, including Christmas morning, and usually eighteen-hour days during lambing, was pretty hard-going. Every four years or so we would have a holiday somewhere up country for a few days. Constant battles with the weather and health did not do much for my father's optimism. It quickly disappeared.

The story was about Rob. I knew that as soon as he mentioned 'the only thing I'd ever experienced which was anything like telepathy with anyone, or anything'. This made it obvious.

Rob, you see, was special. As a sheepdog he was a master of his art; as a person, almost, he left other animals far behind. My father would be first, usually, to rubbish comments on the television about dogs being 'almost human': 'They're not,' he would cry in despair. 'Why do people expect them to be what they're not?'

But he would also be the first to admit that if there was an exception, Rob was it.

Rob was handsome, able and submissive; he wanted to please, which is something which will always make a good working dog or pet, or both. He was friendly – I would spend the occasional hour just sitting in his kennel stroking or tickling him. If we entered his kennel (it was a large, former pig-house and was easy to walk around in) to clean it, he would 'scold' us with a meek, quiet growl, before coming over to be petted.

He had character and intelligence, and something else – something indescribable. Perhaps . . . perhaps it was his kind of magic.

Rob was a long-haired collie in breed, with a rough black coat with a white underside and forelegs, the white hair also stretching up over his nose and half his face, then over the back of his neck like a white woollen head-scarf. His tail had a fairly shaggy white tip, and his ears generally fell carelessly forward or back.

The story which surprised me so much happened a week or so into the Autumn Tupping-Time of 1981, when the rams went in with the ewes to breed, and the ewes needed regular checking to ensure they'd all been attended to by the rams.

Rob was about three years old at this time, and he and my father had been working together for over eighteen months. Rob was the only dog left after Sweep, the other one, had been put down while suffering from cancer of the stomach. All the tasks of the farm were therefore down to Rob. And so, he and my father worked together constantly. All of their tasks became second nature to Rob, even after only a few days; my father needed to give very few orders once Rob was off.

On this occasion they were driving together a flock to be checked from a group of hills covering about one hundred acres which was known as Passeford: a wild, rough collection of hedges and grassy slopes. The ground was wet with the damp of the autumn, but wasn't wet enough to stop the Land-Rover.

The Land-Rover bumped up and over the rutted hills, as Rob, in the back, stuck his nose through a hole in the chewed canvas divider into the cab, and nuzzled my father's shoulder as they looked through the windscreen at the sheep scattering as the vehicle rumbled into their midst. Some of the younger ones still tended to lie, chewing nonchalantly, until the last moment when they had to up and bolt at the sound of the Land-Rover horn.

Then my father noticed one ewe, stumbling around near the hedge, who had a length of barbed-wire caught up in her wool on a hind leg. It was a good six feet of wire, and my father was concerned and murmured, 'I must catch that one,' quietly to himself.

When he reached the corner of the field where he wanted the sheep gathered, he parked up and clambered out of the Land-Rover. Rob jumped down on command and dashed off at once in the usual way to gather the flock, which was scattered about the field, by running along the edge before bringing them in at the end. Hugging the hedge closely, Rob darted expertly along his usual course.

Then my father once again caught sight of the sheep with the barbed-wire trailing from her fleece, and thought once more that he wanted to free her from the wire, and kept his eye on her.

Then he was alarmed to see Rob, suddenly coming away from the hedge well over eighty yards away, gathering in a much smaller group of sheep than usual.

My father was about to shout to keep Rob on course, but he hesitated when he noticed that the pack Rob was guiding towards him contained the sheep with the wire. He kept silent, and watched as Rob brought the pack closer; a few sheep fell out of the pack, but Rob let them go back, concentrating on the sheep with the wire, and parrying its every move to keep it on course, without a single direct command having been given.

Once Rob had brought this group in to my startled father, he waited until commanded to bring in the others, which he then did as perfectly as ever, finishing the job while my father quickly removed the wire from the ewe's fleece.

Rob was an expert – he was usually controlled by whistles as well as straight oral commands, and could recognize not only right and left whistle commands, but the length of the whistle could be varied to say how close the dog should be to the flock. He and my father later went on to compete in several sheepdog trials, winning prizes on more than one occasion.

Once he had performed a task a few times, it became almost habitual to him. That he should then take it upon himself to bring in a specific ewe which my father had made indications, in his mind more than anything else, that he wanted, was almost phenomenal. It certainly never happened to my father with any other dog; but then, he never had such a close relationship with any other dog.

Soon after this my father acquired another dog, Moss, to help manage the huge workload. Some years later, he also got Jack, and then Roy, who was in fact Rob's son and was thus named after the Sir Walter Scott novel *Rob Roy*. He was never as good a sheepdog as Rob, but showed some of his characteristics. Therefore there were four dogs to work the farm.

Consequently the relationship between my father and Rob was never quite the same again. But he was always special, and he kept his magic up until the end.

Rob died of a heart attack, working in the fields, ten years after he and my father had begun working with each other. The vet said it was brought on by a snake-bite – we had noticed that for a few weeks before his death he had lost something: he had been going deaf and had been stumbling when he tried to jump into the back of the Land-Rover, which had to be opened up fully to let him climb in.

It was never the same after Rob had gone. My father, finally battered into submission by this and the other blows he'd been dealt over the years, packed in farming two years afterwards. After twenty years of farming, and the loss of his relationship with Rob, what little magic there had been was gone.

Jennifer Quinn (11)

Mr Moss' Room

Mr Moss beckoned us in
Eyes looking cruelly,
The tambourine me,
So *cruel*
He began a piece,
A funeral kind
Opened up a keyboard box,
Velvet on side
Like a coffin
The blackboard was the hole.

Julia Frost (13)

Learning to Count

Her warm breath puffed down on me,
smelling of coffee and cigarettes.
I stared down at the black printed sum:
5 + 2.
The white Croxley paper
smelt of fish and chips
in salt and vinegar.
Mrs Andrews stared down at me,
a gun ready to fire
if I made a quiver.
As I sat by myself
in the noisy classroom,
fresh Dettol off the table
wafted up on the sweet breeze
snatching it, stealing it.
I stared out into the crisp morning,
my eyes drawing the salt tears.
I blinked, smearing my view
leaving nothing but a wet oil painted picture.
Water trickled down the window,
dropped onto the ledge
and splashed into a small puddle,
making quivering rings twist outwards
into never-ending circles.
The mist slowly moved on,
a slow traveller.
My concentration on the outer world
suddenly shattered.
Seven, seven,
my mind whispered.

Claire Davies (11)

'Seven,' I muttered,
my voice small as a mouse's.
I wrote 'seven',
proudly.
I could feel my heart slowing,
a horse slowing to a trot.
It was over.
I knew how to count.

Rebecca Barr (15)

**Two Summers

The lane was potholed: straightening itself
to the random dips of land and hill,
the right side rising upward to rocks
torn by the hardened veins that trees
bent to the crooked wind.
The left side; sloping its worn ground
to marshland: soft humus and terraced plants
ebbing into watery pools where the reeds
sank together with the mingling tongues
of the forgotten, elder land they knew.

Bounding down the drive to the lane
and leaping round the sinking cracks of tarmac,
we turned our faces to the wind that blew forever
from the empty greying loch and foreign tongue.
Across the field on narrow track, treading
stunted grass of deeper green than ours,
we jumped and sprang from solidity, moving
through our present – smiling to heathered mounds
that threw crickets and blackberries to our open hands.
Wandering the paths where butterflies congealed
rising unperturbed to meet our hands –
no sound was needed. Living was enough.

Elements mixed through time: soil and air
were drawn together by fire from round our hearts –
through life we lived all and everything lived.
Soft air of turf dived on breezes
stirring sun to greater love and summer's colour.
The clouds were so near we could touch them

and feel their nothingness strange to our forms.
Slow moving birds glanced across haystacks
and the man by the stream was holding a scythe.

Tongues slurred a greeting and the pause
we had incurred ended, he stooped again
to the bright straw. We moved on past
the silent pebbles and the whitewashed house
whose open door silenced cold walls whispers
of warmth and winter nights.
Through present we moved and the hills
and mountains far off were crying to the sky
with their cloudy eyes forever, footfalls fell
hard now, onto tarmac; the path had ended
to join another. The cats in the yard were
mewing at our feet; turning, my friend took my hand
and pointed back to the fields and summer's dying sky.

Alastar Mew (15)

Samuel Denham (12)

The Glove

An old glove, leather I think it was,
Sitting on its own.
Seaweed had wrapped it up like a present,
It was worn out, holes all over it.
I couldn't tell where it came from,
Could be from any country in the world,
It had oil all over it, in little patches.
I picked it up, it was full of sand, wet sand,
I didn't think much of it,
So I threw it into the sea,
Now someone else can write about it.

SCHOOL

PRIZE

WINNERS

Three schools were awarded the School Special Award, a new award introduced in 1993, for submitting work of outstanding quality:

St Patrick's Primary School, Armagh, Northern Ireland

Debenham High School, Stowmarket, Suffolk

Handford Hall CP School, Ipswich, Suffolk

The following schools won School Awards for submitting work of the most consistent merit:

Abingdon School, Abingdon, Oxon

Belsize Young Writers, London NW3

Bishop Luffa School, Chichester

Cardiff High School, Cardiff

Central Newcastle High School, Newcastle-Upon-Tyne

Channing School, London N6

Charters School, Sunningdale, Ascot, Berkshire

Chieveley CP School, Chieveley, Newbury, Berkshire

Crawfordton House School, Moniaive, Near Thornhill, Dumfriesshire

Cumnor House School, Haywards Heath, Sussex
Dean Close Junior School, Cheltenham, Glos

Dulwich College Preparatory School, Cranbrook, Kent

Haberdashers' Aske's School for Girls, Elstree, Herts

Halesworth Middle School, Halesworth, Suffolk

Hymers College, Hull

James Allen's Girls' School, London SE22

The King's School, Canterbury, Kent

The London Oratory School, London SW6

Newstead Wood School for Girls, Orpington, Kent

Notting Hill and Ealing High School, London W13

Oxford High School, Oxford, Oxon

Park Hill Junior School, Croydon, Surrey

Pentlepoir CP School, Saundersfoot, Dyfed

Port Regis School, Shaftesbury, Dorset

St Bede's RC High School, Blackburn, Lancs

University College School, London NW3

Wolverley High School, Kidderminster, Worcs

INDEX

* **Award Winners**

** **Special Award Winners**

Illustrators

Joyce, *Richard* *Newman School, Hove,*
East Sussex 1

Kent, *Neil* *Halesworth Middle School, Halesworth,*
Suffolk *156*

King, *Adam* *Halesworth Middle School, Suffolk* 2

* **Kitchener**, Jenny Handford Hall CP School, Ipswich,
Suffolk 169

Knott, *Charles* *Milbourne Lodge Senior School,*
Esher, Surrey *141*

* **Lancaster**, Guy Cumnor House School, Danchill,
Sussex 24

* **Lawson**, Emma Central Newcastle High School,
Newcastle-upon-Tyne 22

* **Lester-Pearson**, Miles Tregelles the Mount School,
York 66

Levinger, *Kate* *Channing School, London N6* *59*

Malpas, *Scott* *Exeter School, Exeter, Devon* 67

McCarthy, *Emma* *Channing School, London N6*
81

MacDonald, *Martin* *Halesworth Middle School,*
Suffolk *161*

McReynolds, Anna Mill Strand Integrated School,
Co Antrim, Northern Ireland 131